Glimpses
into the Past
in Lammermuir.

Other Books by Norrie McLeish

Ancestral Voices – The Story of the McLeish Name
Death in the Borders
The Haunted Borders

As Editor
Glimpses into the Past in Lammermuir (First edition)
Tales of a Grenadier

Work in Progress
Borderline Cases   More murder cases from the Scottish Borders.
Broken Promises   19th century breach of promise cases

Glimpses
into the Past
in Lammermuir.

by John Hutton Browne

Illustrations by William Seton Crosbie

Edited with notes by Norrie McLeish

ALBA PUBLISHING
JEDBURGH

Glimpses into the Past in Lammermuir
John Hutton Browne
Edited by Norrie McLeish
ISBN 1-873708 – 09 -9Z

Published by Alba Publishing 1998
20 Dounehill
Jedburgh
TD8 6LJ

To Sarah, Dylan and Michael,
some of whose ancestors lived and died in the Lammermuirs

List of Illustrations

Contents

Acknowledgments

My thanks are due to all those who encouraged me to bring out a new edition of John Hutton Browne's classic little book. The limited print run of the first edition was rapidly sold out and I am still getting inquiries for it. I have used some of the information from the many people who wrote to me after reading the first edition.

My thanks also to Roy Ledsham for proof-reading the final manuscript and to the staffs of the Scottish Borders Archives at St Mary's Mill in Selkirk, the Scottish National Library and the Scottish Records Office. I am grateful also to the Scottish Borders Archives for their permission in allowing me to reproduce photographs from their collection.

Foreword

I first came across John Hutton Browne's little book almost a decade ago. In 1994 I edited and reprinted this classic Berwickshire work which sold out within six months. It seems to me to be opportune to bring this previously neglected work to the notice of a wider public. Not only does it provide us with insights into the lives and manners of a past way of life; it also allows us to appreciate the writing skill of John Hutton Browne as he weaves his tales of the long-gone folk of this still isolated and relatively unknown part of the Scottish Borders. He wrote only one other book and, as one critic of the time wrote: *"It is to be regretted that he did not take to writing as a young man, he may have bulked much larger in the literary world than he does today."*

John Hutton Browne was born in Kennoway in Fife in 1838. His father was a carrier and his grandfather a ploughman. An able student, he became a pupil teacher at his local school. After this he taught for a while in Stranraer and Lasswade before going to Edinburgh University from 1864-1866. He was appointed schoolmaster in Longformacus in 1866 and remained there until his death in 1913.

It was remarked that he was *"more than the usual type of country schoolmaster"*. He had a well-stocked library and did not care to take part in the village social activities which must have made him appear aloof and somewhat distant in the tight-knit community that was Longformacus at that time. His aim in life, he often declared, was *"to be useful."* He worked hard and was regarded as *"having considerable tact in dealing with the management of children."* I suspect, however, that his real passions were for books and long walks in the surrounding hills. It is impossible not to be struck by his detailed knowledge of the

Lammermuirs as well as by his vivid descriptions of its rivers and glens.

'Glimpses' was published in 1892 and the following year he published *"The Golden Days of Youth – A Fife Village in the Past"*. Its subject was his home village of Kennoway. A critic described it as *"a bright and enchanting volume of old world life in an old world village."* Such a description could equally apply to 'Glimpses.'

He was the last of the old parochial schoolmasters in Longformacus, the last link in a chain of rural schoolmasters who, for good or ill, did so much to shape the minds of the 19th century Scottish peasantry. Many of his pupils were to leave the parish of their birth to seek a new life in the big cities or to join the long lists of emigrants to America, Canada, Australia and New Zealand. John Hutton Browne was to remain in Longformacus until his death. As he was employed by the parish and not by the County Board, there was no compulsory age of retirement. He remained fit and healthy and saw no reason to cease teaching until May 1913 when he decided to hand in his resignation and gave two months notice. One week later, after teaching all day, he had his supper and settled down for his customary nap. He died in his sleep. He had never married and was survived by his sister who had acted as his housekeeper and also as on occasions as an assistant teacher. On her brother's death she left Longformacus and returned to Kennoway.

While retaining the basic structure of the book, I have omitted some of the poems and essays which were in the original 1892 edition as they did not relate to the main themes of Longformacus and the Lammermuirs. I have taken the liberty of shortening some of the author's paragraphs which tended to be rather long by current standards.

I have also researched some of the people and events mentioned in the book. The people who appear in 'Glimpses' were real people who lived, worked and, for the most part, died among the Lammermuir hills. Many of his stories would have come from the memories of the villagers themselves and he is, in most cases, retelling them. I have not been able to track down all of the people mentioned nor all of the events described by the author. Part of the problem is that John Hutton Browne often mixes up dates and times. For example, he has Tom Sherriff, the schoolmaster's son, as a young student at the time of the Peninsular War, at which time he would have been a middle-aged man. The same Tom Sherriff, who plays such a large part in the book, fails to appear in any of the Longformacus records after his birth is recorded. I think he used Tom Sherriff as a literary device to give his "Glimpses" more depth; it seems very likely that the young Tom Sherriff is a reflection of how John Hutton Browne saw his younger self. He does say that these 'Glimpses', *"were built upon the rock of truth, and illumined by the light of imagination"*

He also expressed the hope that at some time in the future, this book would take the reader back to *"a more Primitive time of living in Lammermuir."* I hope that this new edition helps the reader make that journey back through time to catch a few glimpses of people and a way of life which has passed forever.

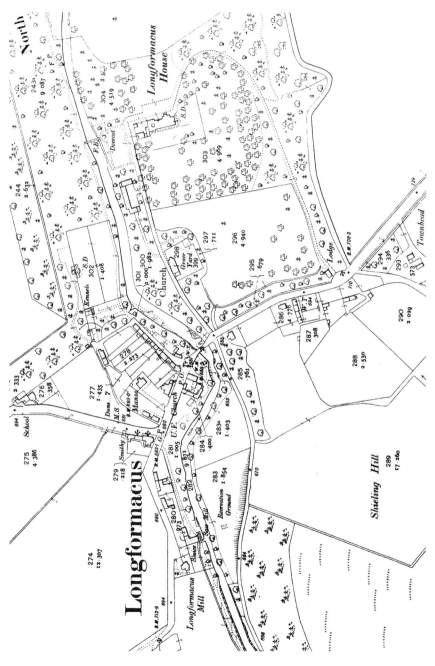

Map of Longformacus

Introduction

The northern slopes of the Lammermuir hills are part of East Lothian while the southern slopes form the northern boundary of Berwickshire. At one time they formed the natural eastern divide between England and Scotland. They are part of a range of hills which sweep in from the west and which begin in the Cheviots. The vale of Gala Water creates a break in this range from which the Lammermuirs stretches eastwards to the sea. A traveller once described them as, *"wild, cheerless, unsightly heights – nowhere bold and imposing in aspect and often subsiding into low rolling table-lands of bleak moor."* In winter, the upland moors can indeed be bleak, inhabited only by sheep, grouse, curlew and the occasional shepherd. In spring and autumn dense fogs can spring up and catch out the unwary traveller. The hills are intersected by a number of rivers which have created small glens or valleys, once bog and marsh, but later cultivated allowing the growth of settlements such as Longformacus and Abbey St Bathans. These rivers also provided a paradise for anglers and for many years the Ellem Inn attracted fishermen from all over the country.

Sheep have from earliest times been the basis of the economy of the Lammermuirs. The name 'lammer' comes from the word 'lamb' as do the names of many other places in these southern hills. There are two 'Wedderlies' two 'Wethers laws' and a 'Wedders lair'. A 'wedder' or 'wether' was a castrated lamb. In addition to this there are Lamb Hill and Sheeppath Glen as well as many others which indicate the importance of sheep to this place.

The present shape of the Hills was created during the ice age when an ice sheet covered the whole area. As the ice started to melt, meltwater streams flowed down from the uplands creating wide channels and gorges. These meltwater streams were often laden with sediment as they flowed under the ice of the lowland areas. As more surface ice melted, the debris remaining formed ridges or 'kames', an example of which can be found in Greenlaw Moor in the foothills of the southern Lammermuirs.

As the ice retreated and the climate became warmer, forest gradually covered the landscape. In the uplands the trees were mainly birch while woodlands of oak predominated in the lower levels. The 'Forest of Lammermuir' provided shelter for a wide range of animals including wild boar, elk, wolf and bear. The arrival of man on this scene, about 9000 years ago, saw the start of the process of erosion which was to create the landscape of grasslands and heather moor with which we are familiar today. Woodlands were cleared for pasture and the raising of crops. Slowly the forest retreated. The arrival of Neolithic man, around 3500BC, accelerated this process. More advanced agricultural techniques had been developed and greater use of domesticated animals was practised. The 'Mutiny' or 'Mittenfu Stones'near Longformacus was built by these incomers. It is a long cairn which served as a collective burial place and was an important feature of an otherwise unknown culture. This is their only monument in the area. There is some evidence to suggest that during the warm and comparatively dry Bronze Age the uplands became inhabited. But over-cultivation and woodland clearance led to widespread erosion and as the climate became cooler and wetter, these sites were abandoned.

The remains of Iron Age hill forts dotted throughout the Lammermuirs mark the arrival of the Celts, who as well as these fortified places, have left their mark in many of the local place names. The major tribe in the Lammermuir area appear to have been the Ottadini or Votadini, as the Romans called them. They had their capital on Traprain law in East Lothian. The glorification of war was a feature of Celtic society with inter-tribal conflict almost a way of life. The Ottadini, however seem to have accepted Roman authority without any great resistance. There are no traces of Roman military roads or encampments in the Lammermuirs. With the abrupt departure of the Romans, the Celts had to face the onslaughts of the Picts and Scots from the north and of the Angles from the south. The Ottadini were absorbed into the kingdom of Gododdin before it was to succumb to the Angles early in the seventh century and the Lammermuir Hills became part of the Anglian kingdom of Bernicia. It would not be until the battle of Carham in 1018 that the eastern frontier between England and Scotland was established at the Tweed.

The hills of Lammermuir became a frontier area in the forefront of the long and bloody struggles with England which lasted, with varying degrees of intensity, until the Union of the Crowns in 1603. At Ellem, deep in the heart of the hills, the Scottish army mustered before setting off in an invasion of northern England. In 1456, Patrick, Lord Hailes, sheriff of Berwick asked that the rents of *"the fermes of Longformacus and Rachburn"* be remitted because of the devastation caused by the English invasion. It was from Ellem in 1513 that the Scottish army gathered together with its artillery and wagon trains before setting off for the field of Flodden a few miles over the Tweed. The return journey over the hills must have been a long and weary one for the survivors of that calamitous battle. The hills were also to provide a barrier to the extension of the king's authority. Here, and throughout the Merse it was the Homes who were the undisputed rulers. That it was a wild and turbulent place is indicated by the ruins of fortified houses and by place-names such as Manslaughter Law where the Earl of Dunbar and Hepburn of Hailes fought a bloody battle.

As always, it was the peasantry who bore the brunt of the violence but they continued to work the land and tried to survive. It had been customary for the farmers to take their sheep up to the high pasture for the summer grazing. There the 'shielings', temporary summer settlements, were established. The commercial development of sheep farming by the Border Abbeys in the 12th century saw many of the 'shielings' established as permanent farms. The warm climate of the 11th to the 14th century gave way to colder temperatures which gradually led to the abandonment of these upland farms. However, improved methods of land cultivation helped some of them survive and their origins are indicated by the use of the suffix '-shiel' in their names.

The rapid development of new agricultural techniques, including the widespread drainage of bog and marsh, changed, not only the landscape but the way people lived and worked in the Lammermuirs. By the middle ages the process of deforestation was almost complete. Wolves, for so long the ancient enemy of the shepherd, had gone as had the beaver, the polecat and the wild deer. The old run-rig method of farming was abandoned and large farms created out of the amalgamation of smaller ones. In the process, many small tenant farmers found themselves reduced to the status of landless labourers and had to depend on seasonal labour in the large farms in order to survive. Most of the people who lived in Longformacus at the end of the 18th century were in this position.

The village of Longformacus, from which the parish takes its name, was regarded as the *"capital of the Lammermuirs"*. In 1384 the Sinclairs of Roslin, who were cousins of the Earls of Orkney, became proprietors of the Barony of 'Longfordmakehous'. This name suggests an Anglian origin, but it may be even older. The British word *'llwcher'* signifies *'a place of pools'*. Above the village the Dye forms a succession of deep pools and in all probability the Anglian name is based on an earlier Celtic place name. At Runklie, about a mile and a half above the village, there are the remains of an ancient Celtic fortification.

Tradition has it that the original Sinclair tower was built half a mile up the Dye from the village on what became known as the Craigie Knowe. There is a tale that a young wife held her child out of a window to let her husband see him as he made his way home from a raid or battle. The child slipped out of her arms and plunged to its death on the rocks below. The heartbroken parents built themselves another home and the tower on Craigie Knowe was abandoned. The present mansion was built in 1715 by Sir Robert Sinclair. Some Jacobite rebels were making their way from Haddington to Kelso and feeling the cold during a stopover at Longformacus, burnt some of the newly-sawn wood intended for the new house. The last of the Longformacus Sinclairs was

Sir Harry Sinclair, known locally as 'Captain Harry'. He was in dire financial straits and, despite borrowing money from many of the locals, had to sell the estate in 1764 to Thomas Raitt, a businessman who had made a fortune in India. During his time many of the small holdings and crofts were 'cleared' and the old 'in' and 'out' field system was discarded. On his death in 1784 the estate was sold to the Home family.

The greater part of the population of the parish were day-labourers, hired servants to farmers or shepherds. They were also desperately poor. Rheumatism and skin disorders were prevalent which the Rev. Selby Ord put down to poor food, damp houses and *"want of cleanliness"*. The minister criticised his flock and he stated that, " *..people accustomed to the pastoral life in their earlier years are rather inclined to indolence and ease."*. However, these were hard times. Perhaps his comments reflected his own prejudices towards a population adjusting to a different type of society from the one that they and the hills had known for centuries.

Part of Longformacus (Sketch)

Glimpse 1.

The last days of autumn were drawing to a close. Parti-coloured October was putting on its farewell smiles, as it often does, before it leaves the stage, and in its warmth and sunshine it seemed to reflect the gracious nature of its sister summer. The harvest was ended in the Lammermuirs, and the carts had joyfully taken the last load to the stackyard. The woods round the village were luxuriant in yellow, brown, and red and now and then a leaf broke from its stem and whirled to the earth, giving token of Nature's fast decay. The morning was Monday and at the door of the primitive schoolhouse, the schoolmaster[1] stood enjoying the freshness and exhilarating air and watching with some anxiety the coming forward of his scholars for the first day's work of the new session. But, as steady work is an institution of civilised life, the tendency of relaxation is towards the old man and so the autumn holidays, with their play and freedom, had taken the relish of self-application from the youths. But in the interval their bone and muscle had grown, as a compensation and a training for the struggle of future years.

As George Sherriff glanced around, a stranger would not have passed him without taking a keen observation at the whole appearance of the man. Dressed according to the fashion of the period in a blue swallow-tailed coat with brass buttons, and in knee-breeches and stockings, he stood in his shoes a tall and handsome man, with thoughtful blue eyes and a ruddy face. On his head he wore a low-crowned hat, and beneath its broad rim there appeared a crop of grey hair that had once been fair. The stout legs that had been able to delve the acre glebe,[2] and make it produce a good crop of potatoes and turnips, were only surpassed by the head that could construe Horace, quote Milton, solve the problems of Euclid, and that could read the New

Testament in its original Greek. The scene of his labours was a mean thatched house with one door and three windows, and was furnished with a desk, three tables, and six seats. His dwelling-house, like the school, was also thatched, and consisted of one storey, and was divided into two apartments. Already the village boys and girls were playing or lounging on the road in front of the school. There were the Niels, the Andersons, the Wilsons, the Mickles, the Blackbells and the Sharps. Followed more slowly by the stragglers from Rawburn, Dimples, Dronshiel, Kippetlaw, Stabswood, Blacksmill, and Otterburn. There were the Brydons, the Guilds, the Moscrips, the Bruces, the Lunams, the Services and the Nisbets.

Betimes Laird Hume [3] appeared round the corner of the road on his shaggy pony, and just as he approached the schoolmaster, Farmer Denholm[4] from Redpath drew up on his way to the smiddy. The three had a friendly chat about the weather, the safety of the crops, and then the conversation gradually drifted to the great war that was raging in the Peninsula,[5] where our troops were driving out the ambitious and unscrupulous Napoleon from the vine-clad hills and orange groves of Spain. Among the villagers the homely laird went by the name of Johnny Hume, whose familiar and kindly ways had won their affections. He lived in a plain style, befitting the extent and value of his lands, and when the winter drew near he migrated to Inveresk for the dark and snowy months. A cart took him and his luggage over the wild road to Haddington and onward. George Denholm was a quiet, pawky Scot, and from his sheep and ewe milk cheese, he piled up year by year a handsome lot of golden guineas.

In the quiet morning, the fragrant smoke of peat arose from the low thatched cottages, and as the youngsters passed on each carried a peat, to lay up a store of fuel for the school fire all the winter. Now George Sherriff entered the school and took up his position at his desk, whose shape and finish may be seen in pictures of the village school of the olden time. He engaged in a fervent prayer for the godly upbringing of his flock. Then he set to work. The elder scholars read a portion of what was then called the Bible, and the younger ones read a portion of the New Testament. Then they waded through the intricate mazes of the Shorter Catechism, or the questions, as they were popularly called. The wisdom of Solomon came in for a fair share of attention, and his Proverbs were taken as a separate lesson. Twice a day this theological fare was imparted to the growing minds, and might account for the grave and thoughtful looks of the Scottish people. No doubt the past of Scotland owes much to its Bible and oatmeal, whatever its future may attain. Arithmetic, with its accurate work and many puzzles, was conducted in seats, and the master with quill and knife prepared pens, ruled copies, and set them for the writing lesson. Before the dinner hour came, a verse of scripture was committed to memory, and this was repeated before the hour of dismissal in the afternoon. As each scholar finished his verse, he marched out for home or play. The standard selection from English authors was called "Mason's Collection," and this was used as a reading book, for spelling, and meaning of words. No work on the grammar of the English language was in use, but many a man has been able to write good English without a knowledge of grammatical rules. However, it was a pity that lessons in geography were not in vogue, as knowledge of the world we live in, like travel, has a liberalising influence on the mind. On Saturdays the school was opened in the forenoon, and again the Shorter Catechism was the substantial fare, which was indeed a skillful preparation for the doctrinal theology embodied in the long sermons of the time. Such was the upbringing and education of the young in the early years of this century, and under the care of a judicious, intelligent, and sympathetic schoolmaster, who will dare to say that it did not bear blessed fruits?

On the afternoon of the first Saturday of school work, as George Sherriff was resting in his little parlour after a plain dinner of mutton broth – very tender mutton, and mealy potatoes, before the terrible blight had extracted their pristine flavour [6] a knock was heard at the door. The shaggy Skye terrier, Dye, gave a sharp bark, but as Mrs Sherriff[7] admitted the Rev. Selby Ord[8], the minister of the parish, Dye wagged his tail and welcomed the visitor. The Rev. Selby Ord was a tall and thin man, with a rather severe aspect, but under his broadcloth there beat a warm heart. At times a sadness stole over his features and grey eyes, and then his parishioners knew that he was reflecting on the disruption between himself and his son, who had given up his University studies, and thrown his life and soul into the occupation of an equestrian in a travelling circus, where he afterwards acquired a reputation for skill and adroitness which still lingers in the minds of many who can recall with delight the ongoings of this memorable show. The two parochial authorities sat and chatted over a little drop of home-made whisky which the schoolmaster had received in a present from William Stark, Whinrigg,9 where he had brewed a peck o' maut in a sly, canny way, though a red-headed Irishman named Tim Maloney had been captured for his share in the transaction.

The mellow sunshine poured in at the small window, bordered on the outside with the boughs of an apple tree, whose red apples peered into the room, and were rivalling the brown tints on the cheeks of Jean Sherriff, who had just told Mr Ord that Baba Bell[10] had been out all night at the Dimples, and that Baba had brought home to Peggy Sherriff or Guild[11] another cherub in the form of a sonsy boy. Barbara Bell, the midwife, she said, had been watched by the boys and girls last night cutting a cabbage stalk from her garden before she departed to fulfil her populating duties. As this news was related, they saw beyond the school garden, a stout young man employed in cutting down some willow wands growing all over a strip of ground which stretched to Birkieknowe. This was Selby Sherriff,[12] the son of the schoolmaster, who was by trade a cooper. The wands were used by him as "girds" for buckets, barrels, luggies, cogies, which he made and sold to customers at home, and at the fairs in town and village. In a little time Mr Ord departed to finish his sermon, and to make one or two calls on the way to the Manse.

As the afternoon advanced, and the hour for tea came on, Mrs Sherriff was heard in her little kitchen among the tea-cups; and when William Redpath[13], the schoolmaster of Langshaws, appeared, he was heartily welcomed by George Sherriff, for then, as now, a kind of freemasonry existed between birds of one feather, and it has been noticed that men of the same profession in each other's company glow and shine much better than in the society of those who have not the password to their open nature. Moreover, Willie Redpath, as George Sherriff sometimes familiarly called his nearest professional brother, was a man of an intelligent and honest nature, and one to be trusted. He was a bright young man and a bachelor, and he was looked upon as a good catch for a Lammermuir lass, and Jean Sherriff had already made up in her own mind a match for the lonely schoolmaster.

The formulation of a widows' fund about this time had a very favourable impression on provident mothers who had a careful eye over their daughters, and when a few friends dropped in to tea from the Mill and the Dimples, it was easily seen how the wind was blowing. They were a merry set at tea, and all reserve was laid aside. They joked and gossiped, and ate their fare in gladness of heart. After tea, a game of cards was proposed, and partners were chosen. William Redpath was taken into partnership with Mary Wilson[14] from the Mill, who had as rosy cheeks and white teeth as ever painter limned. Her eyes were rivals to blue violets and the small plump hand that handled the cards, and the inch or two of arm were sufficient to reveal the perfection of her form. A curious set of counters were used by the players. They were kept in a box of Indian wood and the counters were made up of mother-of-pearl and nicely carved, and were in the form of oblongs, circles, squares, and fishes.

As the evening wore away, the party got into chatting about affairs of the countryside. William Redpath, who had been visiting Priestlaw during his holidays, told the story of the excisemen and the smugglers at Kilmaid.[15] Two excisemen in Haddington had been informed that a small "still" was doing some good work somewhere in Lammermuir, near Priestlaw. They arrived at the farm, and interviewed James Darling,[16] the farmer, who, with unusual coolness, invited the officers into his house to rest and refresh themselves. In the meantime he left the room, and sent one of his trusty men up the Glen to Kilmaid, to warn the smugglers of their danger, and to urge them to pack up their cargo and utensils, and obliterate all marks of their recent work. After doing this, he returned to his guests, and kept them in good humour till he had given the illicit distillers sufficient time to decamp. The excisemen made that day a vain journey from Haddington. Then one of the party from the Dimples told a story about a cadger[17] and his donkey coming upon a "still", on the moor near Cattleshiel, and how his donkey's feet sunk into the turf which covered the excavated ground. The cadger, on his arrival at Dunse, gave the case unto the excisemen. A run was made to the hill, but the wily smugglers had left no trace of their doings behind them.

Again, one told the company of the smuggling that went on at Kilpallat and at Broadcleugh, two miles above Byrecleugh Hill. John Blackbell[18] got notice that the exciseman was coming to Kilpallat, as he met him at the Long Mile. He speedily hastened to the smugglers, and the whisky was hidden somewhere on the Byrecleugh Hill. Robert Munday on one occasion was on his way with a bag of malt to their quarters, when the gaugers[19] were espied, and other tactics had to be pursued to escape them. George Sherriff told them that, when standing at his own door one morning, a man on his way to Dunse came up to him and made him a present of a jar of whisky, and then went on his way.

Such stories helped to while away the night, but before the guests parted, Mary Wilson would read some of their fortunes with the cards. Now Mary, with your nimble fingers, tell the party what you see in the affairs of the rustic Mill. Do you see a quaint couple named Andrew Luke[20] and his wife Helen[21], and a fair daughter of the same name,[22] the dwellers and workers there for many years? Can you tell them how their daughter was cut off in the bloom of her womanhood, and how, after old age came on, the parents followed her and were laid in a quiet spot at the eastern gable of the old church? and how there, year after year, the white roses nod their heads and whisper their mystery over their tombstone? Can you tell the listening party of another hard-working tenant and his wife and son, who spent all their energies on the thankless soil and how on a day in March, when a drifting snow-storm was darkening the sky and filling the air, a company of mourners carried the two aged ones to their last home, where it was soon decorated by the fast-falling snow, and their requiem was the fierce wind through the leafless trees.

Notes - Glimpse I.

[1]. **George Sherriff** (1742-1821). Schoolmaster in Longformacus for 48 years. He had two sons, Thomas (b1777) and Selby (b1784). He also had two daughters, Jean and Christian, who both died in November 1789. George Sherriff was also clerk to the Kirk session for many years.

[2]. **'glebe'.** Portion of cultivable land allocated to a minister in addition to his salary or 'stipend'.

[3]. **Laird Hume.** He was described as a man of strong will who in the greatest of emergencies was never known to seek advice. He claimed that: "I ha'e come to the conclusion, monie a year bye gone, that whan a man pits his property into the hands o' a lawyer, his body into the hands of a doctor, and his soul into the hands of a minister, he had better just lie down in his kail-yard and die."

[4]. **George Denholm.** Farmer at Redpath. His wife was Agnes Virtue. His son, also named George, continued to farm at Redpath.

[5]. **Peninsular War.** 1808-1814. Fought in Spain against Napoleon.

[6]. **Potato blight.** The great potato blight of 1845-46 led to the development of many new disease-resistant strains. It is a not uncommon refrain among the elderly that "food doesn't taste the same as it used to." but in this case there might be some justification.

[7]. **Mrs Sherriff** . (1741-1813). Wife of George Sherriff (see (1) above). Her maiden name was Jean Porteous.

[8]. **Rev. Selby Ord.** (1742-1813). Admitted as minister of Longformacus in 1777. Before this he had been in Cockermouth for 11 years. He is said to have possessed some medical knowledge which would have been of great benefit to his parishioners. His wife was Esher Sargent who died in 1787. He had two daughters; Nancy or Ann, born in 1772 and Margaret, born in 1775, who married John Dods, farmer of Stoneypath in 1808. He had three sons; William who died as an infant in 1780, Edward who was

born in 1779, joined the army and died in 1807 and Thomas born in 1785 (see below). Death obviously came as something of a surprise to the Rev. Ord for he had not made a will. His personal estate was valued after his death at £170. 7. 5.1/2.

[9]. **William Stark.** Wife was Agnes Landlie. They had two daughters; Agnes, born in 1811 and Mary born in 1815. They also had a son, Alexander, who was baptised in 1815. In 1817 the church records comment that William Stark had little work and a numerous family and was given 10/- from the Poor Fund. A few weeks later it was noted that William Stark at Whinrigg had been convicted of aiding and abetting illegal distillation. He was sent to Greenlaw jail for two months. His family became the responsibility of the parish for that period.

[10]. **Baba or Barbara Bell.** Barbara Bell appears in the church accounts records from 1800 to 1834 when she died described as a pauper. She appears to have worked with those on the Poor List as well as being a recipient herself.

[11]. **Peggy or Margaret Sherriff.** She does not seem to have been related to George Sherriff. She married John Guild in 1804.

[12]. **Selby Sherriff.** Born 1784 in Longformacus. Son of George Sherriff, the village schoolmaster. (see above)

[13]. **William Redpath.** William Redpath was the schoolmaster at Cranshaws from 1802 until 1813 when he died. He was unmarried. His estate totalled £46.16.9.

[14]. **Mary Wilson.** In 1873 a Mary Wilson, widow of Robert Hood, farmer, died at Chirnside aged 77. Her parents were George Wilson and Mary Russell. She married Robert Hood in 1822 at Cockburnspath.

[15]. **Whisky smuggling.** Illicit whisky production was a valuable part of the agricultural economy throughout the eighteenth century. The effect of the unpopular Malt Tax of 1725 was to lead to many legal distillers mixing unmalted grain with malted barley which resulted in a product greatly inferior to that produced by the illicit still. For a while illicit whisky production was regarded as an almost patriotic activity and the illicit stills were regarded with approval by almost all sections of society, which made the work of the exciseman much more difficult.

16. **James Darling**. James Darling tenant in Priestlaw who died on the 7th November 1863 at the age of 88. There were Darlings in the Lammermuirs from 1770 and they were tenants of Priestlaw from 1837 to 1958.

17. '**cadger**'. A 'cadger' was an itinerant dealer or peddler.

18. **John Blackbell**. A John Blackbell was born to Walter Blackbell and Christian Kerr in 1797 at Longformacus.

19. '**gauger**'. This was the 18th century term for an exciseman, so called for one of his principal tasks was to gauge or measure the contents of a cask.

20. **Andrew Luke** (1802-1872). Tenant in Longformacus Mill.

21. **Helen Luke.** (1794- 1872). Wife of Andrew Luke above. Her maiden name was Helen Gibson.

22. **Helen Luke.** (1835-1854). daughter of Andrew and Helen Luke above.

The Village Well

Glimpse II

All day long the persistent thud of the flail was heard in the barn at Townhead on that lowering October Wednesday. The Edgars and the Guilds as they left the moor and entered the old road leading to the village and school, listened a minute to its noise, and then recognised its familiar sound. As they approached the farm, they had the curiosity to go forward to the barn, and look over the lower half of the door to see the workers. There, in his shirt-sleeves and red night-cap, the sweat standing on his face, they beheld Robert Currie[1] swinging the flail over a heap of 'singles', or 'gleanings', which his boys had gleaned during the harvest at Rawburn, which was tenanted by the good farmer Peter Purves[2], who allowed all the families of his workers to do as Boaz did to Ruth and the gleaners of old. As Mr Purves wandered behind the shearers and chatted with the bandsters[3], the gleaners followed among the stooks, and sometimes they drew so near the workers that they were now and then reprimanded by Robert Wilson[4.] It was a gladsome time for the youngsters. The fresh hill air, the warm sunshine, the exercise, and the fragrant smell of wild plants sent new life and growth through their young hearts. Besides, they were laying up a good store of oatmeal and barleymeal for the winter food, and they felt an inward satisfaction, that they had done good service to the household, though at times their backs were sore with the bending to pick up the heads of grain. So Robert Currie, a weaver, before he again set foot to treadles and put hand to shutter, threshed out the thrifty produce of his children's hands. The sparrows seemed to know the flail as a source of spoil, for as the schoolboys retired, one or two cautiously left their haunt in the hedge and hopped to the ground near the door, through which grains were driven by the force of the threshing. Then a goodly flock alighted to pick up the stray food.

Perhaps Robert Currie exerted himself beyond his usual strength that day, for Jenny Fortune[5] and Alison Wilson, meeting at the well remarked to each other as they filled their cans that Rab Currie had been going on with the flail since daylight set in, and that there was no ceasing of it. Then they remembered that they would be going to Rawburn that night to keep the 'kirn', or 'maiden'[6] and his heart was joyful and the work was easily to be borne. Tom McLeish[7] had been down with invitations to the shearers and their friends to come up at the darkening. Rawburn was a farm of more limited dimensions than it is now, for Whinrigg, Scarlaw, Fosterside and Dunside have since been added. As the day closed, a brisk wind sprang up from the east, and, in the gloaming, the bright light of the fire from the doors and windows of the smiddy in the Kirk Park shone cheerily around, and the old plane trees, the ashes, and the elms surrounding the churchyard looked weirdly in the dusk, as they shook their boughs and scattered their crisp leaves to the grass below. There was an unusual preparation in the cottages, for most of the families had some connection with the kirn, and they meant to make a night of it.

The river murmured hoarsely as the groups trudged up the road, and crossed the rustic bridge where the gentle Watch meets the Dye. The sough of the wind among the old birch trees and the scamper of startled sheep, caused some of the timid maidens to start aside, and take shelter under the manly wings of John Mack[8] and Robert Wilson, bandsters and elders of the kirk, and men of authority in the eyes of the people. As the party approached the farmhouse of Rawburn, they met others bent on the same purpose, and as they entered the big kitchen they were met by bright light from home-made candles in polished brass candlesticks, and a glow of heat from the big peat fire.

Already a few were assembled, and the tuning of a fiddle was heard. Forms and chairs were set round the room, and the dresser and table were filled with scones, cheese, jugs of ale and a bottle of whisky. In an adjoining parlour, Mr Purves sat at a table, and as each worker stepped into his presence he received by turn his harvest wages, and before the company adjourned to the neighbouring barn for a dance, a song was given by those proficient in the vocal art. William Sharp[9], who had brought his fiddle to play with Tom McLeish was pressed to give a song. Sharp was a man of the middle height and middle age, somewhat thin, but with two bright black eyes, which shone in his pale face, underneath shaggy iron-grey eyebrows. He was by trade a weaver, and his loom at Birkieknowe had been silent during his outing at the harvest. He was by nature a keen sportsman, and the beasts of the wood and the trout of the stream knew him by instinct. So Willie, in a fine clear hearty voice, tuned his fiddle and accompanied himself to *"Neil Gow's Fareweel to the Whisky O!"* – a song that had just been composed in a country manse, and had not been long before the public. As the singer was the first to introduce it to the Lammermuirs, all ears were on the alert:-

"You've surely heard o' famous Neil,
The man that play'd the fiddle weel,
I wat he was a cantie chiel,
And dearly lo'ed the whisky O,
And aye sin he wore the tartan hose
He dearly lo'ed the Athole brose,
And wae was he you may suppose
To bid fareweel to whisky O."

Three blyth lassies from the Highlands, who had finished their work, and were now going home with their hard-earned fee, sang together, "The Bonnie Hoose o' Airlie", and the performance of it by sweet natural voices was enhanced by a certain timidity and shyness. Tom McLeish, Willie Sharp, and Tom Purves, son of the farmer, and a student home from college, now sang with great glee, "Dame Durden," which was applauded on all sides.

It was getting on to the wee short hour when the village party returned home. The sky was obscured with dark clouds hanging low in the atmosphere, and now and then the faint rays of the moon hanging over Whitchester Hill, afforded them just sufficient light to guide them over the watch, and down the side of the Dye towards the bridge. In the manse above a light was seen, and someone remarked that the minister was still at work in his study. A few, groping their way along the row of houses facing the river lest they might stumble into a drain, or come in contact with a peat stack, now adjourned to the house of William Sharp, whose gudewife set aside her spinning-wheel to make room for a crack over the affairs of the 'Kirn' before they all parted for the night.

As George Sherriff, the schoolmaster was coming out of his first sleep, which had been disturbed by his son Thomas[11] busy with his books before going off to Edinburgh University, he heard the pattering of raindrops on the widow panes, and as he listened there were unmistakable signs that a heavy rain was distinctly falling, with set purpose of spending the night in pouring in torrents. The inmates in the village, and every homestead in the Lammermuirs slumbered through the darkness, and opened their eyes to a bright morning, with the face of nature in wood, on hill, field, and moor, glittering with wet. A night's rain on the uplands soon has a visible effect on the river and its tributaries, and as the Dye approached the village it showed its force and bulk as it rolled and tumbled over the submerged rocks. Even the Leipsic Sipe, or runner, collected on the Mill fields, brawled through its tunnel under the public road and school field, and rejoiced in its steep descent to the Dye. The young Niels were out in the morning, testing its swiftness by throwing pieces of wood in at the entrance, and watching them at the outlet. In the forenoon, as John Hope, shepherd on Runklaw, was going his rounds, he saw three persons trying to ford the river a little below Horseupcleugh. They held each others hands as they crossed, but suddenly one of the figures dropped into the water, and was carried downwards. The other two got safely to the bank and were seen to run down the side of the stream. John Herbertson[12], a shepherd on Fosterside, had also witnessed this disaster, and he followed the body as it was rolled onwards. These were the three Highland lassies, who were leaving the district after the harvest. John Hope took in the situation at a glance, and hastened down by the Windygowl and towards the village to give the alarm. The villagers turned out in much excitement. A horse was procured, and John Dunn[13] sat on horseback, in readiness to go into the shallow parts of the current below the bridge, to catch the body as it came down. The unfortunate Celtic lass was borne round the Jackdaw Scaur or Darling's Steps, through the Heron's Hole, over the Cauld, through the deep Nickering Pool, but John Dunn performed his work skillfully, and brought her to the bank, where she lay with pale face and long, disordered black hair.

There was more solemnity in the ringing of the kirk bell on that Sabbath morning. The carts with their occupants from the farms, and the horse with its double burden of farmer and his wife on pad behind, were in unison with the sad occasion. As George Sherriff and his wife and student son, of whom she was proud, turned the key of the schoolhouse door, and walked soberly down the road, they also experienced the gloom which was floating about. Mrs Sherriff was dressed in a black satin gown with short body, and her chubby face looked very becoming in a coal-scuttle bonnet of Tuscan straw. When they crossed the old bridge, they noticed some men and boys from the farms looking over its broken parapet, and when they entered the churchyard, glances were cast at a newly made grave. The Rev. Selby Ord was very serious and devout in his reference to the fatal accident, to the shortness and uncertainty of human life, and the great need of preparation for a swift change. *"Every man must bear his own burden"* was the text of his sermon, which was long remembered by his crowded audience on that memorable day. William Mickle[14,] of the inn, had fewer remarks to make to the farmers as he served them with ale and biscuits after the service, and it seemed to the farmers, but perhaps it was fancy, that the flavour of the ale was changed for the worse.

As Mr Ord took a turn in front of his manse, after tea, he felt very lonely. The river now prattled on, unconscious of its late treachery. Dirrington Law, round and black, lay before him, and the shadows of night were creeping up its sides. He recalled to memory the young and fair wife who had been taken from him years ago. He thought of his gifted son, who was lost to him, though living. He forgot in his anxiety that human nature is many-sided, and that his son in his circus life was administering to a side common to all of them. It was good and honourable work to amuse the people. That night as he sat musing in his study over the past, he pondered over an excursion he had made with his son one summer day into moorland. When they left the manse the morning was fine, and very warm. They walked up the Haddington road and crossed over to the left, and came upon the moss where the minister and the schoolmaster had a right to cast peats for their own use. There was a light haze in the sky and the air, and some fleecy clouds hung about. The muirfowl and moorland birds were making their own peculiar music. The clear cool rill was singing down the hillside, and its banks were adorned with moss, grass and buttercups. Flocks of sheep dotted the valley of the Fasney, and the bleating of the lambs was heard at intervals over the moor. A muirfowl, sitting on the side of the rill, took fright and disappeared over the height. Kilpallat, with its triplet of trees – one ash and two planes – beside the shepherd's cottage, and two men cutting peats, gave an idea of life to the scene. They talked about the lonely lives of those who dwelt in this remote place and pointed to the spot where Mary Torrie, wife of James Torrie[15], a mason, was found dead beside a peat-stack, when she was overcome by a drifting snowstorm. She had left her home in the village, and had gone to Priestlaw to see her son. On her return journey she met this fate. Then they traversed the valley of the Fasney, which is a hill-stream descending through a pretty deep glen, and over a rocky and pebbly bed. The Kilpallat burn joins it a little below the spot where it joins the public road. The rocks of the Fasney are covered with green moss. It has some pretty pools and streams dashing through narrow gullets, where it makes foam and music. Water wagtails sat on the stones, and dipped their beaks in the current. The linties started out of the heather and darted away. Some large trout were hovering in the deep pools. The streams sometimes poured down in foam over a declivity bordered by high boulders, and which resembled a long white horse tail. Fragrant birch and rowan tree ornamented its banks. In the vale of the Whiteadder, as they returned home by Cranshaws, they admired the whin blossom on the numerous whin bushes which clothed the braes, and in the bright sunshine it looked like yellow rich gold.

Next morning, as Jenny Chapman,[16] the aged housekeeper, was lighting a fire in his study, she came upon some writing on a sheet of paper lying on his side table. After some trouble she managed to read it. It ran thus:-

The Gloamin' comes to all

The sun sinks in the west,
The shadows fall around,
The bird sleep in their nest,
Sere leaves lie on the ground.

The heart is sore depressed,
And care drops on me fall;
Morning is oft caressed,
But gloamin comes to all.

The joys of youth are sweet,
The scenes of youth are dear;
After long years friends meet,
And milestones disappear.
We long for a retreat
To let the burden fall
When the waves are at our feet
The gloamin comes to us all.

Notes - Glimpse II

1. **Robert Currie**. (1777-1857). In the 1841 Census, Robert Currie is described as a carrier. Living with him were; his wife, Janet Purves, son, Richard (b1811) who was a tailor, another son, named Robert Simpson, and two daughters, Susan(b1826) and Agnes (b1829). Their other children were: James (b1807), twins Mary and Betty (b1810), Jessie (b1815), Alison (b1817) and Ann (b1820). Robert and Janet were irregularly married at Coldstream in 1805 but their marriage was recognised by the Session in November 1806. In 1833 Robert Currie had to apply for help from the Poor Fund and was awarded 10/-. He and his wife were to receive more help from the Fund in 1848 and 1849. His parents were James Currie, weaver, and Mary Pringle.

2. **Peter Purves.** In 1776 Peter Purves was born to William Purves and his wife Margaret Robertson at Windshiel in the parish of Westruther. In 1800 Peter Purvis and Agnes Collard of Westruther handed in their names for marriage.

3. **'bandster'.** At harvest time a bandster was employed to follow the shearers and bind the crop in sheaves. It provided a useful source of extra income for many of the villagers.

4. **Robert Wilson.** (1762-1850). In 1798 banns were read out in Longformacus kirk for Robert Wilson and Mary Renton. They had five children: James b. 1798, Margaret b. 1800, Alexander b. 1802, Elizabeth b. 1804 and Isabel b 1806. In 1802 Robert Wilson was mentioned as one of the church elders. His wife died in 1835. He was described as being "tenant in Blacksmill" when he died.

5. **Jenny Fortune.** (1786-1855). Probably Janet Fortune, wife of John Fortune, feuar in Longformacus (1784-1869). Her maiden name was Janet Kemp, her father was James Kemp and her mother was Janet Scugall. She had two sons: James, b1816 in Whitchester, and John b. 1824. She also had a daughter, Janet, b. 1814.

6. **'kirn'** or **'maiden'.** One of the key times of the farming year was the successful gathering in of the crop. A successful harvest was a time for relief and for rejoicing and was celebrated on Border farms with a high-spirited social gathering or 'kirn'. The 'maiden' referred to was the last

sheaf gathered in and which was always treated with honour. Sometimes it was shaped into the form of a cross or given human shape. No doubt it has its origins in pre-Christian times.

7. **Tom McLeish.** (1799-1884). Son of John McLeish and Euphemia Graham. he married Agnes Stewart from Lauder. He had four sons: John, Adam, James and Thomas, and one daughter, Euphemia. He was a steadfast believer in the supernatural and was full of stories of witches, ghosts, warlocks, water-wraiths and kelpies. As a shepherd, in his later years, he was well-known throughout the Lammermuirs. He always carried a long staff with an iron pike at the end of it – to protect himself from the 'unco' folk'. He carried in his pouch a kind of white snuff, which he referred to as his 'witch powder'. If cattle were thought to have been bewitched, he would blow the powder into their eyes; people thought to have been suffering from a similar complaint were offered the same treatment. If a hare crossed his path at the start of the day, he turned around and went home. He died at Coltcrooks farm near Earlston.

8. **John Mack.** (1774-1857). at the time of his death he was described as a feuar in Longformacus. His wife was Margaret Dale (1785-1860). They were married at Lamberton in 1809. Their son, Alexander Mack died in 1894 at the age of 64. Another son, Peter, was born at Muirton in 1812. In the 1841 Census the family are at Rigfoot, included are the children; Margaret , aged 20, John , aged 18, Janet, aged 14 and Alexander , then aged 11. they also had a daughter named Isabella. His parents were Peter Mack and Isabella Brown.

9. **William Sharp.** Died in 1810. He is described as having been a feuar in Longformacus for 50 years. In 1791 he married Mary Owen in Longformacus.

10. **Neil Gow.** (1727-1807). Famed fiddler and writer of many Scots tunes, particularly Strathspeys and reels. He began to play the fiddle at the age of 9 and was self-taught until the age of 13. He was born in Strathbraan in Perthshire and was originally trained to be a plaid weaver.

Editor's Note: John McLeish, (the father of Tom McLeish above) was almost certainly also born in Strathbraan. There was a family tradition that when John McLeish left the Strathbraan, he was presented with a brooch for his plaid as a token of friendship from Neil Gow. It became a family heirloom for many years and is now thought to be in Australia.

11. **Thomas Sherriff.** Born 1774. Son of George Sherriff, schoolmaster in Longformacus, In 1805 a Thomas Sherriff married Aleson Edgar in

Cranshaws. In 1806 they were in Ayton where they had twin daughters, Elizabeth and Jane.

12. **John Herbertson.** His son, Robert, died in 1817 at the age of 10. A daughter, Margaret, died in 1842 when she was 2 weeks old.

13. **John Dunn.** (1771-1808). He was the son of Thomas Dun who died in 1793, and Elspeth Hardie who died in 1826. In 1791 John Dun, mason, was rebuked for fighting in public, and on the Sabbath with John and Francis Niel, smiths in Longformacus. In 1789 John Dun and Jean Aitchison appeared before the Kirk Session and were rebuked for their irregular marriage. They had a daughter, Anne b. 1794. It would appear that Jean died young for in 1798 the Kirk Session noted that John Dun, mason, and Elizabeth Howden were married in Edinburgh on May 31st 1798. They had a daughter, Mary, who was born in February 1799. It is possible that he married for a third time as in 1808, a daughter Janet, was born to John Dun and Agnes Niel.

14. **William Mickle.** He may have been the William Mickle who married Ann Murray in 1784 at Chirnside. His father, or possibly his brother may have been John Mickle who died at Longformacus in 1806 at the age of 42.

15 **James and Mary Torrie.** In 1802 James Torry and Marion Waldie had a daughter named Janet in the parish of Westruther. In 1804 they had a son, Robert, and in 1807, another daughter named Agnes. In 1817 we are told that James Torrie was in distress and given a stone of oatmeal. A few months later, he is described as a mason and 'out of employment and in trouble', he was given 10/- from the Poor Fund.

16. **Jenny Chapman.** No trace of a Jenny Chapman could be found. One source says that the housekeeper at the manse was a Mrs Deans. Andrew Wanless (son of the schoolmaster who later became a successful bookseller in the United States) states that, as a child, he *"often sat on auld Jenny Chapman's knee"*. Alexander Deans married Elizabeth Currie in 1808. It is likely that Elizabeth Deans was 'Jenny Chapman', and that this was a 'tea-name' or 'by-name' by which she was familiarly known in the village.

Glimpse III

A sharp frosty wind was racing down North Street, Dunse, on this November afternoon, and as it approached the hostelry named "The Plough", it left sudden gusts to rush up the narrow close, and whirl about the dust and hay in the tiny courtyard behind, where in the stable, a man was muttering words of familiarity to his stout black shaggy pony, as he inserted the bit in its mouth, and fixed the neck-strap. Three boys, who had been on the watch for this performance, came forward as the man and pony made for the street. It seemed that this was not new for them, as man and boys, and even pony, were on friendly terms. Davie Duns held its head, Sandy White clapped it on the neck, and Willie Brown examined the proportions of its bushy and tangled tail. The owner was in the meantime bringing out and fixing on the pony's back a pair of baskets, which he gradually filled with sundry parcels that had been deposited in one of the low-ceilinged rooms of the Dutch-like inn. These were parcels of groceries which had been purchased from Thomas Gray,[2] of the Town House, and Robert Brown, at the foot of Black Bull Wynd. The landlord took out his snuffbox and gave the traveller a pinch of snuff before he departed on his way. Then off he went, and the boys followed on until they came to the entrance of Newton Street, where, with a "Gude day, Willie," "Gude day, Smoutie," they whirled about and made a run for some other diversion.

As Willie Anderson[3] and Smoutie, side by side, trudged forward and turned up the steedway leading to the Lammermuirs, and going in a north-west direction towards Edinburgh, an eye accustomed to comparison might have seen a close similarity between the man and his pony. Years of intimacy might have caused this. Willie Anderson was over the middle height, with a stoop in his shoulders, which agreed well with the bent head of the burdened beast. On Willie's head was a well-worn "Tam-o'-Shanter" bonnet, whose rim blew up now and then with the head wind, and this did not fail to represent the forelock of Smoutie. Both were patient and enduring and silent, except when Willie muttered to himself the details of his load, and tested his memory for the benefit of his home customers. At the foot of that long, unfriendly ascent for man and beast, called the Hardens Hill, both paused to rest, and this occurred again and again during the arduous pull. Before he left the shelter of the old firs, Willie stopped, rested his right shoulder on the saddle, and gazed down into the Merse.

There it lay before him, with its long and broad sweep of farmland, dotted with villages, farm steadings, mansions, and wood, and bounded on the far south by the Cheviots, at whose feet thirteen and fifteen miles away, if his ears could have carried sound as his eyes did sight, he might have heard the Tweed roaring through the bridges of Coldstream and Norham, and then rushing between its banks at Ladykirk, and onwards to the sea, where the waves on the Berwick beach rolled up as if in joy to meet it. If the dusk had come suddenly down, Willie, in his statuesque position, might have started at the appearance of a flaring light far away on the Farne Isles, to caution the watch on the forecastle of a labouring ship miles away at sea, as he gazed forward into the dark and heaving billows.

But now as he reached the highest point of the road, and as he left the lowland landscape behind him, another and not less striking scene, but of a diverse character, burst upon his view. Spread out before him, as if by the hand of an enchanter, was a wild and extensive piece of Highland scenery, and as he rounded the road and pressed forward, its extent increased. The Lammermuirs, in rolling billows of heather hill, and pasture land, stretched for many miles on three sides, and , conspicuous in the distance on the left, was the ancient castle of Hume, and the three peaks of the Eildon Hills due south-west, seventeen miles away. The wind was keen and cold, and right in his face, but yet he gave himself time to halt at Wat's Well, a little beyond the Snuffy Hole, and allow Smoutie to wet its tongue at this perennial spring. Willie was a merciful man, and a merciful man is always merciful to his beast. In the hollows towards Langtonlees, he heard the barking of Wat Stobie's[4] dogs, as they carried out the instructions of their stalwart master. The road was now downwards to the foot of Henley Hill, from which it ran on to a level plain nearly all the way to the 'Strips,' where a slight ascent was made before it dipped into a valley, like the hollow of a hand, in which the village nestled in woods beside the Dye.

As Willie Anderson reached the bottom of Henley Hill, three boys in joyful glee came running forward to meet him. One was his son, Willie[5], and, as he took the reins from his father, he placed the bonnet, which he had been carrying in his hand, on his head. This habit of uncovering his head stuck to him through his life, and when he was up in years, he would walk to Dunse with hat in hand, or work in his sawpit with bare and bald head for hours on a frosty day.

The other boys were Willie Sharp and Jamie Fortune[6]. Away towards Stobswood, a few lights were seen from the windows of the cottages as twilight approached, and if one had been there he might have heard the swish of the 'warping mill', the whir of the 'pirn' wheel, the click of the 'shuttle', and the thud of the 'loom', and in the midst of this varied sound the tender voice of Jim Lunam[7] singing, "*Wae's me for Prince Charlie*", a sad refrain which might be in keeping with the dreary round of his daily work. As they passed the gate leading to Blacksmill, and began to descend the hollow, where flows the burn of that name, Willie Sharp drew the attention of the others to the smell of burnt malt from the kiln there. The 'Strips' or long avenue of sombre firs was restless in the breeze, and through its swaying branches a sound, not unlike the lashing of the waves on a sandy shore, had a saddening influence on the spirits. Little did these boys think that some of their children grown up would see a stronger and more fatal breeze tossing scores of these favoured pines to the ground, like straws before the foot of man.

When they approached the village they met James Melrose[8], tailor, entering it from the east, and he stood an instant and told Willie that he had been 'whipping the cat' at Deukdubs for John Mack the farmer, who was getting a suit of fancy corduroys and a blazing red waistcoat to go to the Dunse markets. Jamie Fortune hid behind the backs of the others, as he saw Betty Umpherston[9] with her cats at the door. She was considered a kind of witch by some of the villagers, and the illness of a cow, or the want of milk from it, was ascribed to the evil influence of Betty. But the boys who often bothered her, cared for none of these things. It was owing to some mischief towards her that he concealed himself. When Smoutie crossed the bridge and came to its master's house and shop, they saw George Sherriff, and Willie Anderson hasten to unburden the pony, and unpack the baskets, which among other commodities contained the schoolmaster's snuff. Young Willie was at once sent by his mother to the manse with Mr Ord's tobacco, not forgetting a 'pickle' to Jenny Chapman, who like her master, had discovered the soothing effect of a pipe at night and in solitude.

Night soon settled down upon the village, and lights from the windows shot out into the darkness, which was partially lit up by the numerous stars from a frosty sky. The imps of mischief which ministered at the shrine of Hallowe'en were abroad, and in the garden plots, boys were cutting down the stalks of cabbage for their abominable sacrifice. The same three boys who had met Willie Anderson on the road, were now laying their heads together in consultation for the night's diversions. Opposite Bob Dale's house stood his peat-stack, and it was the habit of Nell[10], his wife, to go to the front of the stack and lay in a supply of peats for the night. The boys knew this. The boys took a few of these peats to a quiet corner, and made holes in them with their knives. Willie Sharp, who had stealthily brought his father's powder flask, dropped a small quantity of the powder into all the holes, and covered them up. They then replaced them in a position where Nell Dale was likely to lift them on the first occasion. When this was done, they hurried off to the Kirk Park, and prepared their cabbage stalks. They cut off a piece about six inches long, and scooped out its soft inside, and in the hollow they inserted a piece of tow. This was set on fire at one end, which was placed at the keyhole of a door, and, by blowing into the other end, the house that was operated on was filled with smoke. In a short time the smell and the smoke in the house soon warned the inmates of their situation. But, when they tried to open the door, behold it was fastened on the outside. The imps, of course, enjoyed the rage of those inside the longer and greater it increased, until some neighbour or wayfarer put an end to it. So these three peered into the smiddy, illuminated with the blazing fire, which Robert Niel[11], blacksmith, was blowing up for the horse-shoes, coulters, and chains ready for his deft handiwork. A pair of horses from Comfortlees were waiting their turn, and several ploughmen were lounging about and chatting with Bob Dale[12], who was resting on a bench after his day's work at Otterburn. He had been helping Geordie Miller to smear his sheep with Archangel tar and melted foreign butter. They mixed the tar and butter in tubs, and rubbed the mixture into the skin of the sheep with their hands to keep it clean and healthy. His hands were as black as those of an African, and, as he had that very night carried from Otterburn an empty tar-barrel, for the purpose of using the staves of it for torches when he went out to leister the sea-trout, the colour of his hands was heightened. The boys, however, managed to light their 'smeekers' and depart. Betty Umpherston's keyhole was tried first, and, as she soon experienced the 'smeeking', the muttered curses on their young heads were fast and furious. But, fortunately for Betty, John Fortune[13] happened to pass on his way to the tailor's , and the urchins scampered off in various directions, to meet again gradually for further mischief. As the evening advanced, Bob Dale found himself at his cosy fireside, which consisted of an open hearth, round which members of his family might sit. The fire of peats lay on a stone hearth and from the roof hung a chain, to which the cooking utensils were fixed. The smoke of the fire ascended through the open chimney above. Nell Dale was busy making bannocks, and as she kneaded out the dough, and shaped the bannocks, they were laid on the hot stone and covered up with red burning peat. When they had time to be fired, they were taken out and cleaned with a brush. The fire, however, needed to be renewed. Nell put on a few peats. Bob was warming his feet, and looking on at his wife's manipulations of the bannocks, but he nearly leapt out of his chair when puff, puff, went the gunpowder in the peats, which were tossed out of their places as if by some supernatural force.

But this was not the last of the imps' daring. The habits and peculiarities of the dwellers of a village are soon known and spread among themselves. As Bob Dale, an outdoor worker, was an early riser, it was his custom to open the door and scan the sky for the state of the weather. The three boys, prowling about the secret places of the village, had fallen upon the tar barrel. They waited their opportunity. The barrel was placed against Dale's door, and cautiously filled with water, and in such a position that it would fall inwards when the door was opened. By and by the lights disappeared from every window. The stars looked down upon the peaceful scene. The only signs of life were the ever-murmuring Dye, the sounds of wind through the branches of the trees, and the cry of the owls in the Caldside wood. Morning drew on, and no premonition of danger warned Bob Dale of the mishap which was about to befall him. He opened the door, a great rush of cold frosty water poured in upon his bare legs, and drenched both him and the cold clay floor. Bob did the best thing in the circumstances. He jumped into bed and comforted himself, on what we nowadays call hydropathic principles.

About the time that George Sherriff was going into the school for the day's work, two women were seen from his window making for the schoolhouse. They were in close conversation on some engrossing topic, from the excited gestures of head and hands which they exhibited. Mrs Sherriff had hardly time to usher them into the presence of the schoolmaster, when they were making protests and lamentations about the conduct of these 'blackguard callants' at their houses the previous night. The complainers were Nell Dale and Betty Umpherston. When George Sherriff took his seat at the school, in his well-worn stuff-bottomed armchair, he glanced round the benches, and he observed that three of the village boys were absent. From this he formed his own conclusions. So the peat fire blazed away, and warmed up the room, with its damp clay floor, for the comfort of the scholars on this rather frosty morning, when cold feet and chill fingers were not in keeping with the handling of pencils and slates.

As the Rev. Selby Ord was engaged at the manse during the day pruning his old apple trees and gooseberry bushes, he now and then raised his head to listen to a peculiar sound of some heavy material rolling down to the river, and afterwards followed by laughter and shouting. These were the three imps of Hallowe'en, who were now playing truant and amusing themselves at Craigie, where the remains of an old quarry afforded them great pieces of stone, which they rolled down the side of the steep brae towards the Dye. Craigie in summer and autumn was adorned with long grass, primroses and foxgloves, and bunches of ferns, but now it was divested of this beauty. However, the careless boys exulted in the bounding stones, increasing in rapidity as they dashed into the water below. In the evening they were taxed with their fault, and they confessed it. In order to amend matters a little with the schoolmaster, old Willie Sharp and Willie Anderson arranged to leister a trout for him. Sharp during the afternoon, had noticed two large trout lying in a pool near the bridge. As darkness came on, Willie Anderson took a lantern, and Willie Sharp took a ' five ta'ed leister', and they examined the spot. There they were side by side, with their heads up water. Sharp speared one, and dragged it to the bank. He returned to its neighbour, which lay unmoved. This was also speared. In a very short time they were in the possession of Mrs. Sherriff, who gave her husband a gentle hint to be 'canny' with the boys.

During the night there was a slight fall of snow – the first fall of the year, and hill, moor, and field were in dazzling white as the morning sun shone through the frosty air. The scholars from the village crowded round the peat fire, while those from the farms came glowing with warmth. George Sherriff after prayer made a statement about the case of the truants, and appeared to be very severe, though in his heart he felt a kind of sympathy for the shortcomings of boyhood, and in his mild blue eyes there was revealed to the close observer a twinkle of fun. However, the usual punishment must be enforced. The three culprits were accordingly summoned to the floor, in front of the master's desk. George Sherriff took from his desk a small log of wood, to which was fixed a short chain. This log was tied to the right foot of Willie Sharp. The schoolmaster then turned to the wall for wig and broad-brimmed hat where they hung, but lo! they were not there. It turned out that they had fallen to the floor the previous day, and that the little dog Dye in roaming about the school at the dinner-hour for 'pieces' had seized the wig and hat and had inflicted on them considerable damage. Mrs. Sherriff had taken them into the house for repairs. In a little time, then, Willie Sharp was robed in wig and hat, and in this state he marched up and down the school to the great amusement of his fellow scholars, to whom he made obeisance when they passed him. The other two boys underwent the same ordeal during the day.

That evening, George Sherriff stepped up to the manse to have a chat with the minister about the news of the parish. Jenny Chapman was full of talk about a new visitor to the manse, and the Rev. Selby Ord chimed in with her. It seemed that a pair of robins had taken up their abode in a high, thick, old wall, the remains of some old mansion, covered with ivy, on the west side of the manse gardens; and as the morning was cold and the ground covered with snow, the male robin came peering and hopping into the kitchen door. Jenny gave it crumbs and enticed it into the house, where it made itself, in a little time, quite at home. It perched on the table, chirped, and turned its head first to the right and then to the left, and peered at Jenny, and then at the minister, with an intelligence that meant to say, *"I know the state of matters here, and I mean to come regularly and do my duty."* When it became tired it went off to its mate. That night as the Rev. Selby Ord and Janet knelt in prayers in the study, Jenny, with a woman's instinct, discovered that the tiny messenger had already taken possession of a corner of the minister's heart. He was not more earnest in his devotions, but his earnestness was mingled with a softness which was formerly awanting, and when he prayed for kindness and protection to all God's creatures, this softness was especially marked.

Notes - Glimpse III

1. **Davie Duns** (b1812). Son of David Duns and Helen White who were married in 1804 in Duns.

2. **Thomas Gray** (1783-1871) feuer in Duns. His wife was Agnes Garven (1786-1862). they had a daughter, Fanny, who died in infancy. Another daughter, Janet, died in 1829 aged 17. A son, John, died in Brazil aged 29.

3. **Willie Anderson**. (1789 – 1859). His first wife was Ann Philips whom he married in 1816 and who died in 1828 at the age of 40. In 1816 she was paid for cleaning the church. He then married Jane Colvin who died in 1871 at the age of 67. In the 1841 Census he is described as a joiner living with his wife Jane, and children; William aged 18, John aged 9, James aged 7, Alexander aged 4, Thomas aged 3 and Robert aged 3 months. He also had a daughter, Elizabeth, who was born in 1816. Willie's father was William Anderson who was the Kirk Beadle in the early 1800s and who died in 1819. His mother was Elizabeth Tod. Willie was also the village undertaker. His death in 1859 is described as being a result of *"a shock to the system"*, caused by a fall. He had another son, Henry, who took up his father's undertaking duties.

4. **Wat Stobie.** A Walter Stobie was a shepherd at Redpath in 1851 when he was 25. He was born in Coldingham and had two children: Walter, born in 1857 at Redpath and Elizabeth, born in 1859 at Kippetlaw. His wife was Mary Haliburton. The Wat Stobie referred to here was probably his father who, with his wife Jenny, lived in a lonely spot at Blackrig.

5. **Willie Anderson Junior.** (1822 – 1854). Son of Willie Anderson (3) above. He died at Roberton outside Hawick.

6. **Jamie Fortune.** A James Fortune is mentioned in the 1841 Census and is described as an agricultural labourer aged 55. His wife was Euphemia Rutherford (1798 – 1869) whom he married in 1820. They had 5 children at the time of the 1841 Census: George aged 19, Janet aged 10, Thoms

aged 7, Euphemia aged 6 and Elizabeth aged 2. Janet died in Australia in 1855. However, Jamie could also have been the James Fortune (1811 – 1886) who married Janet Wilson at Longformacus in 1837.

7. **Jim Lunam.** He was born in Abbey St. Bathans in 1805. In the 1851 Census he is described as a labourer living with his wife, Elizabeth, and their children, Janet and David.

8. **James Melrose.** His wife was Betty Wilson. Their children were: Robert, born in 1792, John, born 1796, Alison, born 1798 and another Robert born in 1800. The first Robert had presumably died.

9. **Betty Umpherston**. In 1833 Betty Umpherston got 10/- from the Poor Funds. She may be the Margaret Umpherston whose husband, John Mickle, a tenant in Longformacus, died in 1806 at the age of 42. They had two sons: David, born in 1787 and Alexander, born in 1797.

10. **Nell Dale.** (1794 – 1869). Helen Dale, born in Greenlaw. Wife of Robert Dale. Her parents were George Middlemis, who was a shepherd, and Marian Berry. When she died in Greenlaw she was described as a pauper.

11. **Robert Niel.** (1795 – 1864). His wife was Helen Dalgliesh and they had 4 children: John born 1821, Margaret born 1823, Henry born 1824, and James born 1829. His parents were John Niel, blacksmith and Janet Lunam. At the time of his death he is described as an innkeeper having previously followed the traditional family occupation of blacksmith.

12. **Bob Dale.** Aged 55 in the 1841 Census where he is described as an agricultural labourer. Two children are mentioned: Alison aged 14 and Alexander aged 11. In 1803 beacons had been placed on the summits of hills throughout the Borders to warn of invasion by the French. One was accidentally lit and it set off a chain reaction which caused militia groups throughout the Borders to muster. Great excitement prevailed. The Dunse Volunteers armed themselves and started to march to Haddington. As they passed through Longformacus Jean Carpenter tried to join them armed with a rapidly cooling, red-hot poker. It was only with the greatest difficulty that Bob Dale persuaded her to return to her house.

13. **John Fortune.** (1784 – 1869). Son of James Fortune and Sibelly Moffat. His wife was Janet Kemp. (See Notes Glimpse 2).

Glimpse IV.

The day's work was at an end. The last boy, who had just repeated his paraphrase, gathered together his books and slate, and tin flask for his dinner milk, and placed them in a leathern bag, and took his departure. George Sherriff was at peace. But even now the hum of his little active world was in his ears, though the actors had gone, for the custom of allowing all the young tongues to wag at work prevailed here as elsewhere; and as the hum of bee fills the ear, and seems to remain there, although the bee has departed, so it was with the human hive. The schoolmaster now drew forward his chair to the yet glowing fire, and, like a king in seclusion, began to reflect on the present, past and future of his affairs. He had that day received by the hand of Robert Waldie, carrier from Edinburgh and Gifford, a newspaper called *The Edinburgh Courant,* in which his son had marked with pen the death of an old scholar among the list killed in the war in Spain, and this circumstance had set his thoughts in a pensive groove. The week's work, too, had been uphill. The weather had been wet and blustering, and altogether unsettled, until this day, and the scholars had been kept at home at the farms. The progress was hindered, and he felt this drawback the more, as he was anxiously working up his school for the annual examination before a deputation of ministers from the Presbytery. A few months yet elapsed before this great occasion in the annals of the school. One boy, in whom he had discovered mental ability of sterling value, was reading Euclid and Horace admirably, and he was bent on his making a dashing appearance. Only today, as the boy was translating the ninth ode of the First Book of Horace, George Sherriff became quite gushing and enthusiastic over it, and compared Dirrington Law with snowy top to

Soracte, the glowing peat fire in the cosy farmhouse, with its various comforts and winter amusements among the lads and lasses, to the old Roman life which the poet described, and which keep his writings still green, as human nature in its essence is unchangeable.

As he gazed into the peat fire, his reflections were now and then broken by sudden gusts of wind banging the ill-appointed door, and making shrill whistling through the keyhole. He thought of the years he had spent in this quiet rural retreat far from the busy world. He thought of those who had come to him, young and toddling things with eyes full of wonder at the new life which they were going to begin, how they had grown in body and mind under his charge, how they had gone into the world, with all its cares and occupations, how they had got homes of their own and families, and how their own boys and girls had been stamped with his impress. It was the third generation that was under his care. His nature was bright, and he was in the habit of looking at the sunny side of life, and it gave him supreme delight to see his old scholars, as handsome young women and strong young men, return to him with a smile of pleasure and a hearty shake of the hand. To their memories many of the little tiffs of school life would be vividly recalled, but from the old master's they had disappeared. But this thought came oftener to him now than in the past, that he was fast treading the lower paths of the other side of the hill of life. He could not conceal from himself that his best days were over; for though still hale and hearty, an inward voice spoke this to him in unmistakable language. And at these times, such thoughts as the mystery of life, which puzzles all minds, would come upon him with overpowering weight. As he now turned his eyes to the school window, a scene in keeping with his thoughts struck him forcibly. The weather now settled was uncommonly mild for the time of the year. The western sky near the setting sun was beautiful with tints of orange, purple, and gold, and in the pale blue above floated clouds as if in a blue sea. Against all this the long, uncut twigs of the double hedge in front of the school, and the trees and landscape from manse road to Rawburn, stood out clear and well defined. To the old man's mind the scene acted as a Jacob's ladder.

But in the midst of his philosophy he was suddenly startled by the entrance of a boy into the room, who exclaimed, "Oh, maister, there's a horse o'er the brig." So George Sherriff rolled up his newspaper, put on his broad-brimmed hat, and hurried down to the bridge, but in his haste he did not forget to take out his horn snuffbox and take a pinch of Taddy. As he rounded a corner of the road going downhill, he saw some villagers standing and looking earnestly at some unusual proceeding at the old parapet of the bridge. A cart was set aside, and in its shafts hung the remains of a horse's harness. When he looked into the river, there lay on the rocks and the water flowing over it a cart horse dead. As the carter was coming down the hill from Townhead, and as he approached the bridge, the horse took fright, it might be from the shinty playing of the scholars, and reared to the side and bolted over the low parapet of the bridge, where it hung, and the poor animal had to be released from this position by losing its life. After years of patient work without the gift of complaining at any hard treatment it might have suffered at the hands of thoughtless and inconsiderate management, the faithful worker met this tragic death. In a small village, where events are much alike all the year, this one threw over it a cloud.

George Sherriff pursued his way along the row facing the river and turned up to Birkieknowe, where he called on William Sharp. Sharp's wife welcomed him with a courtesy, as it was considered the proper manners in those days, and showed him into the workshop, where he had an occasional talk with the weaver. Willie was also in a thoughtful mood this afternoon. He was sitting at his loom with his elbows resting on the breast beam, and his hands on the side of his head. Sharp was a philosopher and a politician in his way; and though he did not reveal always his mind to his neighbours, or even to the minister, he opened it up to George Sherriff on subjects such as the Scriptures, the government of the country, and the social life of the nation. The French Revolution had sent its disturbing wave of thought over the whole of civilised Europe, and into this quiet corner it was even felt. So Willie Sharp might be called one of the advanced men of the village. The schoolmaster said to him in joke, "*Well, Willie, what are you going to do with the bishops now in*

Parliament?" "*Kick them out of it and be hanged to them.*" The sunset of a winter's evening was forcing its way through the small window of his shop, and as he sat there at his loom he appeared with his thin face, and grey hair and eager, black eyes, a perfect embodiment of a revolutionist. Then they compared the mildness of the weather with the snow of the previous year, and spoke of the hunt which Willie had after a hare which he saw from his window in the school field. He got his gun and followed it up the Haddington road, past Horseupcleugh-road end, over the moor, past the grey mare and the grey mare's foal - huge stones in moor and on road resembling these animals in recumbent position - then towards Duddo bank and near Kilpallat, where he killed it within sound of the swift and noisy Fasney. Before the schoolmaster left, he informed him that he intended to have some sport with his "leister" before long. So George Sherriff left the weaver at his loom with his radical thoughts in fermentation, and when he reached home the Rev. Selby Ord was there waiting him.

Next week was the "Sacrament Week", or the "Preachings", as it was sometimes called, and the minister was full of study and business. He had to make arrangements for the service on the Fast Day, the Saturday, the Sunday, and the Monday; and after talking matters over with George Sherriff, one of his elders, he went off in haste.

That evening Robert Currie called at Sharp's, and they with Bob Dale arranged to have a night's sport on the Whiteadder, as the big trout had run up the streams, even to the village, and were seen in their old haunts by old hands in sufficient abundance to entice them away so as to fill the larder for weeks to come. Then they set to work to prepare torches from the staves of old tar barrels. They split these into thin pieces and wrapped them in pieces of old sacks steeped in tar, and tied the whole with bands of string. The night was quiet and starry as they left the village about ten o'clock with torches, leisters, and rope and sack. When they crossed the rustic bridge at Blacksmill burn they noticed a large trout floundering in the shallow stream, but they pursued their way to Hudscleugh, where they heard the Dye rushing in the hollow; and as they reached the tableland at Whitchester, with its open and breezy outlook over a wide expanse of Lammermuir, they saw lights on the river Whiteadder at Ravenscraig below Fellcleugh, and remarks were interchanged about John Dodds[1] and his "merry men" being out for a take. Then there was no need for disguise in the form of blackened faces, and no extra hands were put on as watchers, and there were no water baillies to run the risk of being immersed in a pool, and sent home to bed until their drenched suits were dried. All was fair game between the fish and the spearman. At the Ellem Inn[2] that famed resort for anglers, they called halt and went in to have a chat with the landlord, an old sergeant, who had seen active service in Flanders, and who could spin a yarn to keep his hearers to the small hours over the flowing bowl. When they got to Barnside, they turned their heads up the water and set to work. Willie Sharp took the three-taed leister in hand, Bob Currie carried the torch, and Bob Dale kept himself in readiness for the care and capture of the fish. The first two waded in the water; and as the bright and flaring light reflected on the water, and showed the trout lying at rest on the gravelly bottom of the deep pool, down went the leister, and the fish was secured and thrown to the bank. When they got to Greenhope the night's work had succeeded well, and when they arrived at the junction of the Dye with Whiteadder, the rope upon which Bob Dale had strung the trout and drawn through the water for ease in their transport was getting weighty. After capturing a few in the pools there, they gave up the sport. Away at the farmhouse of Ellemford, they saw a light in one of the windows, and they knew Robert Hood[3] would be up to see his men go off to Dunbar market, with their horses laden with sacks of oats on their backs, for which they would get six shillings for each sack. They tumbled the fish into the sack, and hurried home just as the streaks of light were creeping into the eastern horizon. Their take was divided into three parts, and a few were used in a fresh state, and the remainder were pickled or kippered for winter food.

About this time outdoor workers were about the end of their labour for the season. They hung about the village and did any odd job for a neighbour or their own household, but there was no regular employment until spring. The fish of the river, the beasts of the field, the fowls of the air, the flesh of the pig, and it may be the produce of the cow, and the meal and potatoes, afforded the family a comfortable living during the severe weather of winter. A farmer now and then invited a few villagers to bring their guns to his turnip fields to shoot a few hares, as the hares were doing more damage to the turnips than their value. George Denholm of Redpath would stand in one of his fields, and give instructions to the sportsmen, as they surrounded the turnips, to get a good bag for their own use. About this time a party had been over; and George Denholm, after taking possession of a hare for his own use, selected a plump one to be taken to the Manse for the elders' dinner. When it was handed in, Jenny Chapman had her hands full with cleaning and general preparation for the visit of the ministers. The Rev. Selby Ord, when not engaged on his Scriptural studies, spent an hour in cleaning up the walks of his garden and grounds. The old leaves were raked and the weeds were uprooted. One day, as he was thus employed, he turned to make use of his wheelbarrow, and to his surprise and pleasure there sat the robin upon its edge. It had become more tame every day, and it was a regular inmate of the manse, going now into different rooms. This was its first approach as he worked in the open air. The lady robin did not altogether approve of this absence and neglect on the part of her lord, for more than once she had come to the window of the dining room and dashed herself upon the glass and pecked at the pane with her beak as much as to say, *"Come home to your own family,"* just as a jealous or thrifty wife would search for her husband in a neighbour's house, or in the village inn, where good fellowship and cheer had laid hold of his affections.

On Thursday, the Fast day for the half-yearly Communion, came the Rev. Dr Bowmaker [4] from the neighbouring parish of Drinkwell on his stout grey cob, which felt the weight of its rider, as he was a man about sixteen stone. He was fair and florid, with fresh red cheeks and white teeth, and his manner was gracious and frank, and at the same time full of dignity. His head was bald, and polished like a billiard ball, except on the sides, where grew tufts of fair grey hair. His sermons, though not conspicuous for much originality of thought or expression, were pleasing from the fine modulated voice and exact pronunciation of the speaker. He seemed to be a thorough student of Johnson's Dictionary. In early life he had been a chaplain in the navy, and this might account for all the suavity which had attracted towards him the liking of young and old of all ranks in his own parish. On Saturday came the Rev. James Johnston,[5] minister of the neighbouring parish of Langshaws, who, in this remote district, was, to some extent, a light in darkness. He was a man over the middle height, with a round bullet head, and a habit of winking his blue eyes that might have been injured from the lonely life which he spent as a bachelor over his books. He had a fine taste for the classics, and it was he that George Sherriff feared most on the day of the examination, lest he might puzzle his Latin scholars. In the pulpit he was quiet, and his discourses were carefully written with the proper mixtures of the Law and Gospel common to sermons of the period.

On Sunday came in the afternoon, the Rev. John Sked[6], minister of the neighbouring parish of Abbey St. Swithins. He rode up in time to take the duties of the third table. He was a little slender man, wiry, with bushy iron-grey hair, rather disordered, and wore glasses, through which his grey eyes peered keenly. His speech was quick, and his sermons were inclined to be adorned with the flowers of rhetoric. He also officiated on the Monday. On the Sunday the church was well filled, and the whole service was characterised by a solemnity which seemed to pervade the spirit of all engaged in it. On the occasion of the winter "preachings" there was no outdoor speaking, but in the warm sunshine of July it was the custom for one of the ministers to take his stand on the landing of the outside stair leading to the east gallery, and expound the word to a gathering of hearers standing below among the tombstones of the churchyard. Staples were sunk in the sides of the door, and rods were fastened to these, over which a piece of canvas was stretched to keep the sun from the head of the preacher. An outdoor service was sometimes given from the front of the "Big House." Thus at the same time three discourses were going on. The minister in the kirk might be giving an address on the "Sermon in the Wilderness," the minister on the kirk stair might be giving one on the "Manna," and the minister at the front of the "Big House" might be giving one on the "Pillar of Cloud by Day," and the "Pillar of Fire by Night". At that season the picturesque avenue or lane leading from the bridge to the kirk was rich in its summer greenery, and was sprinkled with knots of men and women who were going to or coming from the inn, where refreshments were liberally supplied by the obliging landlord. The dinner for ministers and elders was given on the Monday at the manse, and a novice at this festival might have been surprised at the change of tone which had come over the company. They were full of jocularity and banter, and they all appeared to enjoy the well-cooked dinner which was neatly placed before them by Jenny Chapman. When the cloth was removed, the mahogany was so well polished that the port, and the claret, and sherry decanters in going their rounds had their images reflected in the wood like ships on smooth water. The Rev. John Sked was tortured about willow wands until he had to laugh again. It seemed it was his favourite amusement to employ his spare time making "creels", and on a Sunday morning he was found at the work, having forgotten the day of the week until his absence from church at the appointed time took one of his elders into the Manse and there he was at his "creels". The robin was present on the sideboard, and was a subject of great interest, especially to genial Dr Bowmaker.

During the week the Rev. Selby Ord visited those who had been unable to attend the Communion; and, of course, from other members of his flock he heard their opinions on the strange ministers, their texts, and exposition of them. One evening he was rather late in returning home, as he had been at Cattleshiel, and leaving the moor and entering the village in the dusk, he was relieved by the sight of the living habitations with their lighted windows and their look of homely comfort. As he passed along he heard the sound of a loom or the noise of a spinning wheel, at which nimble hands were converting to thread the flax of their own growing. It had been laid in the lint holes in the field on the east side of the village and beside the Dye, and after the various processes in its preparation it was now being turned into thread. The smiddy had its knot of loungers, and the tailor's and shoemaker's were visited by those intent on business or gossip. The pedlar was in the village with his pack of goods and news. The Rev. Selby Ord called in upon the miller who was at work by candle-light, and he heard the water lashing over the great revolving wheel as it turned the huge millstones to grind the Lammermuir oats and barley. Indeed, the minister was inquiring when his glebe oats would be converted into meal, for you must know that Jenny Chapman and he took a supper of porridge and fresh new milk, the produce of his own cow, and the minister sometimes thought it was a dainty dish to set before a king.

Longformacus Church (Sketch)

Notes - Glimpse IV

[1]. **John Dodds.** (1779 - 1856). His parents were Alexander Dodds and Isabella Bertram. In the 1851 census for Longformacus he is described as a farmer of 440 acres at Fellcleugh. He married Margaret Ord, the daughter of the Rev. Selby Ord, in 1808. Their children were: Alexander (b.1824), William (b.1829), Isabella (b.1831), John (b.1833) and Margaret (b.1836).

[2]. **Ellem Inn.** This famous old inn was situated at the junction of the Whiteadder and Blackadder and was very popular with anglers. The Ellem Fishing Club was formed in 1827.

[3]. **Robert Hood.** Possibly the son of William Hood and Marion Bertram. In the 1841 Census he is described as a farmer at Elmford aged 20. His wife was Margaret Weatherly who died in 1849 at the age of 28. In the same year their two young children, John and Margaret, also died. 1849 was not a good year for Robert Hood.

[4]. **Rev. Dr. Bowmaker**. (1731-1797). Was ordained by the Presbytery of Chirnside and had intended to emigrate to America. He became minister at Duns in 1769. In 1787 Robert Burns visited Duns and heard Dr Bowmaker preach. He had chosen a sermon in which obstinate sinners were denounced. Burns noticed that Miss Ainslie, his host's sister, was concentrating very hard on the sermon. The poet scribbled a few lines and handed them to her:

"Fair maid, you need not take the hint,
Nor idle texts pursue.
T'was guilty sinners that he meant, not angels such as you."

Burns noted in his diary that the minister was: "*A man of strong lungs and pretty judicious remark; but ill skilled in propriety, and altogether unconscious of the want of it*". He died in 1797 while visiting Berrywell near Duns. His wife was Mary Watson (1748-1816). They had two children: Jean, who was born in 1768 and Alexander, who was born in 1777 and who became a wine merchant.

[5]. **Rev. James Johnston**. (1764-1851). Ordained in 1792 at Cranshaws. Translated to Moffat in 1801. He married Jane Murray in 1795. After her death in 1812, he married Alison Anderson with whom he had five children.

[6]. **Rev. John Sked.** (1736-1813). He married Margaret Renton (1766-1796) in 1790. They had two children: Margaret, born in 1791 and William born in 1792. It was said that in order to eke out his scanty living, the Rev. Sked made and sold baskets.

The Manse at Longformacus

Watch and Dye

Glimpse V

Adam Street in the Scottish Metropolis is within a stone's throw of the University, and consequently was favoured by students who had to betake to lodgings. Walking eastwards and on the left hand side of the street, there is a main door with railing in front of the windows, and between the railing and the wall there is a narrow patch of earth covered with tufts of dirty grass to remind townsfolk that there is such a thing as "country". Into this main door a tall stripling was entering with books in hand, and as he pushed through a long passage to a back room - bed and sitting room in one - he threw his books down on the table, and said to his landlady, who was mending the fire, that they might rest for a few weeks. It was the New Year's recess and he was going to the country to his old home. The landlady smiled, for her intercourse with the student lads had not been little. She was tall and thin and dark, with a melancholy cast of countenance, and Tom Sherriff's student friends sometimes said that if she were put into a wig and gown, and sat down on the bench, she would pass for a Judge of Session. This back room looked into a small green, and sometimes Tom was visited by a large black cat, which came to the window and looked at him with its large yellow eyes. Tom (that is the student) had been but a few months in town, but they seemed like years. He was yet homesick, and the longing to see again the heather hills and the village in the hollow, and to hear the music of the river, was still strong upon him. Each week he went down to the Calton to see the carrier to get news of the place, and by him the messages and letters were sent home. By this means the box made by the hands of the village joiner brought to him the home produce carefully packed by his anxious mother. On the afternoon of this day he went off to arrange with the carrier about going out to East Lothian, and then crossing the Lammermuir Hills. The journey was slow and tedious, but the carrier and his dog were amusing companions, and the people and places on the way afforded sufficient interest to an observant youth. When Tom Sherriff arrived at Gifford he did not wait till the carrier was ready to continue the journey, but hurried over the hills. The weather was sharp and bracing, and he enjoyed the free open moorland road as he swung his arms up the hill after leaving Danskine, where he refreshed himself by a draught of new milk and a piece of oatcake. As he was marching up the Redstanerigg, near the Gipsy's grave, he met the Gifford doctor on his pony. He had been at Mayshiel all the night, and Tom Sherriff, after exchanging friendly salutations with him, knew that the population of the Lammermuirs was now increased by one.

At the Fasney bridge he rested and looked over into the hill stream brawling down the glen, and in the hollow a flock of wild ducks took fright, and hastened on to their haunts near the Whitadder. Just as he was watching their flight, a voice behind him made him turn. It was that of William Darling[1], of Millknowe, and afterwards of Priestlaw, where his name was known far and near for his shrewdness and genial hospitality. As these two sat and talked, they little thought of the tragedy that would be enacted near them in a brief period of time. The air was chill, and the heather, with its withered and dead aspect, was depressing. The sun too shone out with stilted rays, and it needed smart walking to keep his youthful blood in comfortable circulation. A thrill of gladness passed over him when he arrived at a point of the road where the valleys of the Dye and Whiteadder came in sight. When he got within sight of Cranshaws, and the farm homesteads in the left valley, he almost ran for joy. Indeed, he threw his hat in the air, and took up stones and flung them about in very gladness of heart. There, far away in the distance, stood the Twinlaw cairns, over those billowy moorland heights, and looking like two stumps of old trees. There were the Dirringtons, big and little, guarding the entrance to the valley of the Dye, nearly straight in front of him, and down in the hollow on the right sat Horseupcleugh, nodding itself to sleep as it listened to the sound of the river. Far away the road to Dunse was seen winding over the uplands like a great cable thrown at random. On the left, the Whitadder was racing past Cranshaws Kirk and School, and down towards Ellemford, where in the winter sunshine it looked like the mainspring of a watch torn out and twisted, and laid flat and glistening like blue steel.

As Tom Sherriff neared the village and saw Townhead and the upper cottages, his joy burst out in song, and it was only when he espied a shepherd making for his direction with long swinging steps that he ceased his song. At the Caldside gate he saw a person coming up the hill accompanied by a shaggy dog. This turned out to be his mother and Dye. She had espied him coming down the hill, and as she welcomed him in a subdued fashion, there was in her eye and voice an undercurrent of deep feeling. Dye was cautious at first, but when he began to recognise his young master his delight knew no bounds, and at times his joy seemed too much for his full heart. Away in Adam Street, Tom had during the last few months thought over this journey and his meeting, and how everything would appear to him - the trees on the roadside, the fields, the school, the domestic fowls, and the stones in the Dye, where, as a boy, he had been want to jump, and sit, and watch the ripples of the water as they went dancing down in the warm autumn sunshine. The favourite fishing pools too, with their rippling outlet of tiny wavelets, ran in his head, and the holidays by the singing stream were delicious to think of, and he would see them again once more, though in the chilly season of winter

Next day Tom Sherriff went over the old familiar ground, and renewed his friendship with old and young in the place. He had a long talk with Willie Sharp about the city of Edinburgh, the University, with its professors, his studies and the student life; and just as he was going away, Willie Sharp, who was now at his kitchen fire, turned sharply round, and said, in an insinuating voice, *"Tom, did you ever hear me sing?"* This was Willie's favourite method of introducing a "turn" at the music. So the fiddle was brought out, and a song or two went round. Tom was not so shy now, so he gave Willie a touch of the student's style of melody.

At this time the winter afternoons soon came to an end, when the sun drew down suddenly, and night drew over earth its dark veil. The fire was then the best flower in the garden, and round the warm hearth the family were bright and cheery. One evening the inmates of the schoolhouse were engaged in their several occupations. George Sherriff was absorbed in reading *"Childe Harold"*[2], a poem which had been lately published, and which had made its author famous. Tom had brought it from Edinburgh University Library for his own reading during the holidays. The fascinating language tinged with melancholy enchained the schoolmaster and bore him through the Cantos; Mrs Sherriff was winding some worsted into a clue with the help of her son. She was working a "comforter" or muffler for him before he returned to the city. As he held out his hands he watched the two cats of the house playing on the front of the bookcase. The young one was perched on the top of a row of books, and it was looking over at its mother below. The two now and then sparred with their paws, and when the mother was too severe on its daughter the latter took shelter behind the books. But soon its head was peering over like a shy maiden at the window over a balcony. Tom Sherriff was watching their movements, and as he held the hank of worsted he fancied he could make the kitten go to sleep behind the books, and make it have in its dreams a conversation with the poets, introducing their traits of character and style of language into the dialogue. But his thoughts on this subject were interrupted by the entrance of two stalwart young men with crooks in their hands and plaids round their shoulders. The dogs were left between doors lest they might make a disturbance in the social circle inside. There was a degree of shyness about them which George Sherriff at first could not account for, but the reason flashed upon him, and he in a jocular way set them at their ease, especially Robert Moffat[3], who was the principal in the affair. He gave in his name and that of his "intended" for Proclamation of Banns of Marriage, that is, he was to be "cried" on Sunday, and this was his "best man" he had brought with him. After the news of the district had been discussed, Robert Moffat invited in the customary manner George Sherriff down to the Inn to drink his health and happiness. When they got out of doors and wended their way down the road towards the village, they found that the stars were out and a keen frost had set in.

> *The frosty winter day is at its close,*
> *Ice gathers on the river as it flows,*
> *In bush and ivy wall, and last year's nest,*
> *The shivering birds betake themselves to rest,*

Like bits of glass on road the ice pools stand,
Hard ridges run like cords o'er grass and land.

As they turned into the door of the Inn they heard the tinkling sound of the Dye as it carried its frosty waters through the bridge. There was a glowing fire in the large public-room with its low ceiling of wood, and they drew round the table near the hearth, and made themselves cheery. A gracious smile of welcome lighted up the ruddy face of William Mickle the landlord, as he set refreshments before his customers. As the liquor began to warm the blood, and stimulate the brain, those of colder temperament began to thaw, and allow their natures to radiate. So stories were told, and songs were sung, and the laughter was loud and hearty. During a lull in the hilarity they heard the moaning of the frosty wind, and the rushing of the Dye, and the door of the room opened, when in walked three strapping soldiers in uniform. They had walked from the Borders, and were on their way to Edinburgh Castle, but they were going to sleep at the Inn that night. A soldier is always a welcome guest; and if he has been engaged on active service, his company is the more welcome, as his experience in battle, and knowledge of strange countries, give a double interest to him. Before the evening was over, the health of Robert Moffat, shepherd, was proposed by George Sherriff, who was always ready to see all the good points of his old scholars. Robert replied, and sung the following song of his own composition, in a very fair baritone voice, which was cheered by all:-

The Lass o' Evelaw Tower.

The primrose peeps upon the brae,
The sun blinks on the moor,
The birds are cheery on the tree,
For Spring is at the door.
When gloamin' veils a' nature round,
And silent is the hour,
I spiel the hill by singin' rill
To the Lass o' Evelaw Tower.

The stars above shoot beams of love,
With hope to beckon me,
And o'er the way the breezes stray

Wi' message from the lea.
When at my glance her blue eyes dance,
She kens I'm in her power,
For Cupid's dart has played its part
For the Lass o' Evelaw Tower.

The rose at morn on dewy thorn
Is fair and fresh to see,
The heather bloom some eyes may plume,
And blossom on the tree;
But the fairest rose that shepherd knows,
Will bloom by Dye's fair bower,
Soon by my side she'll be my bride -
The lass o' Evelaw Tower.

When George Sherriff returned home the frost was still keen, and the sky was studded with multitudinous stars. A wind was wailing round his house, and even inside the feeling was winter indeed. On the forenoon of the following day, as he stood at his door, he waved a farewell to the three soldiers as they marched smartly past the school, and soon disappeared over the ridge on the Haddington road. The road and fields were as hard as bone. About half-past eleven o'clock a darkness appeared in the north-east, and some round snowdrops came pattering down. The darkness increased, and the snow increased, and the storm was full upon the village. The scholars who had been out for play, and who were warming themselves up by running up and down the road, were now called in. The school seemed under the power of twilight. The snow fell in large flakes. The scholars from the farms were sent home. As the day wore on the wind increased, and the drifting of the snow was great. Some carts from the farms had gone to Dunse, and men from the village set out with shovels to help them home through the snow. As Mrs Sherriff was looking out of her window in the afternoon, she was surprised to see a wayfarer pass the schoolhouse and going towards the village. It was Meg Mawse from Muirton on her way to the grocer's to purchase some tobacco for her own use. She rested in Willie Anderson's, and before night came on retraced her steps homewards. As she approached the entrance of the road leading to Muirton, the drift was so powdery that she wandered past and kept up the hill towards Redpath. She was never seen alive again. The family at Muirton waited long and late for her. The door of the box-bed was opened and the bed was ready for her, but as night drew on the anxious inmates at last concluded that her friends at the village had detained her there. The three soldiers had a fierce contest with the drifting snow on the open moorland road. They fought bravely with the elements over the heights as far as Kilpallat and the Fasney bridge, and in the hope of reaching some human habitation as they descended to the lowlands they still persevered. They no longer marched abreast, but each one struggled through the deep drifting snow as he best could. Near the Gypsy's Grave and the Redstanerigg the battle was ended. Overcome as by an enemy they were afterwards found, the one a few yards in front of the other, as if they had been slain in the battlefield. Thank God, the end came to them in peace.

Next morning, as George Sherriff opened his door, he was met by a wreath of snow reaching up to his arms, and the road in front was completely blocked. As Meg Mawse had not returned home, a search was made for her, and by the side of an old quarry hole, about a quarter of a mile from the entrance she should have taken, they found her resting peacefully with the winter sun shining on her placid brow, and her right hand in her pocket grasping the small parcel of tobacco. The ruling passion was strong in death. A few days after this Tom Sherriff waded over the crisp snow and looked into the smiddy, where a group of loungers were talking about the news of the district. It seemed from what was said that a shepherd belonging to Priestlaw had fallen over a steep bank into a wreath of snow and had perished. A pawky shepherd at Rawburn who had experience of snowstorms coolly wrapped himself in his plaid and lay down during the drifting. In the bright sunshine of the winter morning they found him sitting at the side of a peat-hag, forming his mouth into shape for whistling a tune, and to make a favourable impression on those who were in search for him.

The flight of some rooks towards the old plane-trees in the churchyard, where they settled to examine their old nests, now turned the conversation. Some compared the rooks to the clergy, and from the clergy, the talk drifted to the iron "jougs" that were hanging on the wall of the old kirk. Some dispute arose about their use. A wag proposed that they should try them on Adam Edgar from Dirrington[4.] So a few of the men jumped over the wall, and the collar of iron, with chain attached, was put round Adam's neck and fixed. The others ran off. About this time a tall, thin woman, named Tibby Rankine[5], might have been seen walking stealthily down the kirk road. She carried something in her apron, but when she got well down the lane she peeped first to the right, then to the left, before she flung crumbs of bread on to the snow to the birds, which seemed to be quite at home in her presence, for they hopped about and picked up the food. Tibby was considered strange by some, who even called her a witch. James Hall[6], who occupied the "Big House" when the laird was at Inveresk, now turned the corner, and at that moment they both heard the sound of distress issuing from the kirkyard. James went in by the small gate, and he found Adam Edgar trying his best to free himself from the "jougs". Adam did not submit himself to church discipline again. The chain and a piece of the iron collar still hang there, rusty and wearing away by time and weather. The old sun-dial on the gable-end above measures the coming and going of the sun. The old plane-tree with its weight and wealth of branches stands opposite, but the hands that played the practical joke on the young farmer of Dirrington, and the hearts that enjoyed the fun therefrom, are still forever.

Notes.- Glimpse V

[1]. **William Darling**. Born at Millknowe in 1778 and died at Priestlaw in 1883. He was for over 40 years the factor of extensive estates in Caithness.

[2]. **'Childe Harold'** The famous epic poem by Lord Byron was published in three parts; in 1812, 1816 and 1818.

[3]. **Robert Moffat**. (1814-1885). Shepherd at Trottingshaw. He was born in East Lothian. Jean Knox appears to have been his second wife. He had three children with his first wife, Mary: John (b.1840), Archibald (b.1844) and Mary (b.1848). His parents were John Moffat, and Agnes Wilson.

[4]. **Adam Edgar.** His wife was Jane Kerr who died in 1847 at the age of 67. They were married at Coldingham in 1808. Two of their sons died young, probably Adam, born in 1821 and James born in 1811. They had a daughter, Helen, who died in Edinburgh at the age of 30.

[5]. **Tibby Rankine.** (1776-1856). Elizabeth Rankine, her father was John Rankine, a shepherd in Dayshaugh who died in 1828. Her mother was Helen Allan who died in 1826. In the 1841 Census Elizabeth Rankine is described as having been born in Longformacus and as having 'independent means'. However, she had to resort to the poor Law funds in 1833, 1841 and again in 1846. She may have been the Mrs Rankin, widow of Robert Rankin of Cattleshiel, who applied for poor Relief for herself and her four children.

[6]. **James Hall.** In the 1841 Census he is described as an agricultural labourer in Windilaw, aged 55. He lived with his wife, Mary, and their seven children: Mary (b.1821), John (b.1825), Peter (b.1827), Thomas (b.1830), Agnes (b.1833), Elizabeth (b.1835) and a baby of four weeks who at the time appeared to be nameless.

The Village Row

Glimpse VI

The morning was ushered in by heavy showers of rain borne on a blustering western wind, and in the forenoon these were followed by an artillery of haildrops, which were again succeeded in the afternoon by a fall of snow. The trees overhanging the river were powdered in the evening with white, and its black waters ran through banks clothed with white robes. The moor too was white, except where the black wet heather had melted the flakes of snow as they fell, and on those parts it seemed as if the moorland had shaken itself clear of this burden. The top and sides of Dirrington Law were seen in whiteness. The temperature was so low, as darkness came on, that there was a prospect of ice for the morning. But the weather-cock, like earthly potentates, has a knack of wheeling round in unexpected quarters, and when daylight came in a thaw accompanied it. The day turned out raw and cold, so cold that the damp air seemed to penetrate the flesh and hang there. The trees lost their white powder, and the moor regained its bleak aspect. The roads ran with streams of water, and the open drains in the village, and every rivulet near sent their waters into the Dye, now pouring down strong-coloured currents not unlike a mixture of coffee and milk, with the milk in greater proportion than the coffee.

The good folks of the cottages kept beside their fires, and few heads were seen at the doors that day, until a voice was heard singing at the end of the row in a high-pitched key, and with quavering tones, a Scotch ballad called the "Lass of Glenshea." As the person, who was of sailor-like appearance, sang and moved along the front of the houses, doors were opened, and men, women, and children came out to listen. After he had finished this he recited "Watty and Meg," the production of Alexander Wilson[1], the Paisley poet, and when he came to the verses describing the scolding wife, the matrons at the door hung back, and tittered behind their aprons. The singer was well advanced in years. He was dressed in a well-worn suit of blue clothes, with a blue cap on his head. He carried in his left hand a bunch of ballads, like the columns of a newspaper cut up and laid upon each other. These he sold to his hearers. They were the street ballads of the time. In his pocket he carried a collection of "chap-books", such as "History of Buckhaven", the "History of Mansie Waugh", or more serious works, as the "Pilgrim's Progress", the "History of Joseph and his Brethren" done in verse, and embellished with quaint woodcuts. The curious boys and girls came out, and followed the minstrel along the doors, and up towards the school, and hung about him till they saw where he was going to get shelter for the night. They heard George Sherriff telling him that he could get a lodging for the night at Dirrington farm, for Adam Edgar had a kind of open house for the outcast. Cobble Davy, for that was the name by which this broken-down sailor was known, was directed towards the loaning at Townhead, which led to the moor and towards the farm. As Jean Edgar was inspecting the cows at the watering-trough, she observed a dark figure somewhat lame coming towards the house. The collie ran out to salute it, but she called it off, and after some remark, Cobble Davy was taken into the kitchen, where he underwent many cross-questions from the farmer and his wife. The boys sat and listened, and inwardly digested the appearance of the sailor, and his rambling knowledge of the outside world. This was the first visit, but the honest and generous nature of the homeless wanderer took their fancy, and they kept him there for months together, doing odd jobs on the farm. When he got wearied of the monotony of the moorlands, he would shoulder his small knapsack, his chap-books, and his ballads, and go off on his country rounds. After an interval of some months he would again appear, and set to work as a cowherd, a worker in the hay or harvest field. The young Edgars were fascinated by him, and the young Guilds, from the Dimples, though shy before him at first, got to like the stories of his seafaring life, and the ballads and chap-books were to all a mine of imaginative literature, which they did not soon forget.

In the summer evenings he made for them a small schooner, with masts, rigging, and sails. It had a deck with hatchways, and a tiny helm, and a keel of lead for the purpose of ballast. Cobble Davy would sometimes be seated on the grass near the well of sparkling water, and he would teach the boys gathered around him the names of the sails, and other parts of the ship, so that young Adam Edgar soon had at the point of his tongue the terms from the jib to the mizzen-spanker. He had the name Pretty Jane painted in red letters on its bow. When the school vacation had come, Cobble Davy, after the work at the peat-ricking and hay-making, would accompany the boys to the lake at the foot of Dirrington Law, and there they would launch the Pretty Jane on the rippling waters, and watch its gallant course as it sailed to the eastern side, from which flowed the stream then called Lake, but now the Dronshiel Burn. The industrious spade of James Fortune [2] had not yet cut a water-way to drain this lake, and send its waters hurrying down the glen.

Jean Edgar, from the window of the farmhouse on the hillside, would witness the amusement of the "callants" as she sat at her knitting, and sometimes her heart would misgive her at the thought of her son Adam's love for ships, stories of adventure in strange countries, and the wonderful hold that the perils of the deep had upon him. There she sat, with the purple bloom of the heather before her eyes; the evening sun was glistening the waters, and sparkling the rivulet as it meandered through the meadow in its devious way to the Dye. Away towards Stabswood and Blacksmill the smoke was ascending from the chimneys of many cottages, betokening the inside comforts at the close of a day's hard work. Above her head and on the wall hung a few prints peculiar to the times. In the canonical colours of red, blue, and yellow, was seen Elijah throwing over Elisha in the field his prophetic mantle. In another, Elijah was ascending into heaven in a fiery chariot drawn by horses. In another was a scene from the history of Joseph - the jealous brothers selling the favourite son to the Ishmaelites. Sometimes she would catch her son reading such stories as "Robinson Crusoe" and "Gulliver's Travels," as he lay in a hammock which he and Cobble Davy had constructed out of old sacks, and had hung upon the beams of the horse-mill. He imagined that the two Laws were like the icebergs which the sailor had seen in the voyages he had made to Greenland for whale fishing, and that the Kyle Hill far away in the background beyond Cattleshiel was the mainland covered with ice and snow. Sometimes he would say that the Laws resembled the great mountain waves which Davy had described to him, and which he had seen in the great storms during his voyages across the Atlantic. He had come and gone on various occasions. He had sung his ballads and recited his "Watty and Meg" on a certain day in the month of February, and as he stood in front of the schoolhouse, he noticed two men going in and coming out of the school, as though employed in some kind of work. He had the curiosity to look into the room when his recitation was finished, and there he discovered that the men were laying the floor with turf. Then he remembered that they were making preparations for the cock-fighting which was the customary amusement on Fasten's E'en[3]. In the village, and at the farms, the best cocks had been selected for weeks before this, to be especially fed and trained for this carnival, and the schoolmaster was now looking forward to his perquisites in the form of entry money, and the beaten birds. Davy was well received that night at Dirrington, and with the aid of the young moon in the shape of a sickle bent towards the west in a cold leaden sky, with twinkling stars, the young Edgars insisted on going into one of the outhouses to let him see what they considered would turn out to be the champion cock. That night the wanderer, glad of a settled resting place for a few months, sang himself to sleep in his humble bed in the neighbouring stable.

The following day was one of sunshine for early spring. The sun about mid-day shone on the moorlands, the lake, and the Dirringtons, through a thin haze hanging over them, as on a day in summer. Wet drops, sparkling like beadwork, hung on the mossy grass, the heather, and the fragments of wool torn from the fleece of the sheep. But patches of snow still lay on the great Law reminding one that winter was not far out of sight. It was indeed a charming morn, and so thought the daughters of the farmer of Cattleshiel, for they were in a cart seated on sacks of straw, and on their way to the kirk. The Edgars saluted them as the cart was driven smartly along the road, on the face of the brae skirting Dirrington and the Dimples, and going on towards the loaning near Townhead. The driver of the cart was James Stockwell, a tall muscular young man of twenty years, and it was rumoured that he had an eye on one of the farmer's daughters, expecting by and bye to become tenant of a Lammermuir farm, when he would take her as its mistress.

As the hour of noon passed, and the kirk bell had ceased its sound, a knock was heard at the door of Dirrington farmhouse. This turned out to be the return of the Cattleshiel party. According to their statement, James Stockwell had stopped the cart in the loaning, and without any explanation had loosened the catch of the "coup cart," and had landed them into the dirty road. The reason for this strange proceeding was never fathomed.

On the morning of the carnival of Fasten's E'en, no little excitement was experienced in the village, and at the farms which were to take part in the holiday. Some of the cocks belonging to the villagers had been sent to a "gang" at the farms, for more freedom to gain growth and strength. They had been kept there since Handsel Monday[4]. For two weeks before the carnival they were put into a dark crib and fed with boiled barley. On the appointed day George Sherriff was abroad, and waiting for the gathering. They came with the cocks in sacks or in baskets. The little school was gradually packed with adults and scholars, and when the latter could not obtain a full view of the scene, they tried to do so by peering through the legs of the men in front of the [5]. Two cocks from Blacksmill and Whitchester were first chosen by lottery. The "handlers", who instigated the animals to combat, placed them on the turf, and held them close to each other. When they began to peck at each other, the "handlers" set them down. The savage sport then began. One of them turned out to be a "wheeler". It ran round in a circle, and then it turned suddenly on its antagonist and inserted its spurs in its head. This ended the first fight. The onlookers did not seem to realise there was anything out of place in this issue, from the critical remarks which were made about the conduct of the pair. The next cock was one from Dyeshaugh. They began at once, and after some brave work, the one from Whitchester lost its senses, and lay on the turf. To give this one a chance of rising, a hundred was counted by tens. When the counter came to ten, he called out, "once told", and when he counted another ten, he called out, "twice told", and so on until he came to "ten times told". But when the half hundred were counted, up sprang the Whitchester cock and set to work again. This fight was considered a "draw". In these curious amusements steel heels were sometimes fixed on the birds, and when one was used against the head of another, it went through it like a needle. They sometimes killed themselves by mischance with this instrument. On some occasions both cocks would go on fighting stone-blind. When the sport was ended, the schoolmaster had a good supply of fowls on hand. He did not feel in any way out of place in this affair, as custom hangs round our necks like a mill-stone, and the conventionalities of life choke the avenues to many a fine feeling. But a little incident tended to prick the armour and bring in reform. The Blacksmill cock was killed and taken into the schoolhouse. James Service, its owner, stood outside crying for the loss of his favourite bird. He cried so much that it was hard to comfort him. But, by degrees, they took him away to the field in front of the "big house," where the rest of the day was to be spent in a game of football. George Sherriff did not forget the grief of this blue-eyed boy, and the cause of it.

The game of football was a fierce onset between the villagers and the farm people, and boys were in danger of getting themselves hurt in the midst of kicking men, regardless of the consequences of their strong boots shod with iron. Cobble Davy took charge of the Edgars and the Guilds, and in the gloaming he conducted them homewards. But it was well on in the night before silence was restored to the village, and not a few legs and shins felt acute pain that night in going to bed.

The carnival was over, and several days had gone by, when two stout tramps, on their way across the country to Haddington, called at the school door and requested help of the schoolmaster, who was in the thick of preparation for the coming examination of his school. The Scripture knowledge and the Shorter Catechism work was going on. He invited the men to enter the school, and to the astonishment of the scholars he placed a catechism in the hands of one of the men, at the same time asking him if he could answer the question, " What is effectual calling?" He and his comrade could not answer it. George Sherriff then offered a penny to the one who could learn it. The bigger of the two set to work, but the other pulled him by the coat-tail, and whispered, "Come away, it is not worth the money". He, however, stumbled through it, and effectually earned his penny.

This incident was rehearsed to the Rev. Selby Ord with great gusto, one evening, as the two officials sat in the manse and arranged matters for the examination. At last the eventful day came. It was a morning of much anxiety to George Sherriff, who enjoyed little sleep during the night, and who took a poor breakfast. Though his scholars were well prepared, as he thought, and though he had undergone this ordeal over and over again, the human mind could not be acclimatised to it, so to speak. The scholars came in their best. The farmers and their wives and daughters were there in force. They were to dine at the manse after the examination. The three ministers were the Rev. Selby Ord, the Rev. James Johnston, and the Rev. John Sked. George Sherriff went over a wide field of Scripture knowledge and the scholars in that department made a most creditable appearance. The Rev. John Sked examined the highest reading class, and its intelligence was much commended by the examiner. The Rev. James Johnston gave the boy great credit for his translation of the 1st Book of Horace, and for his accuracy in demonstrating the forty-seventh proposition of the 1st Book of Euclid. He clapped him on the shoulder, and joked about his having successfully passed the Pons Asinorum. George Sherriff was glad when the various classes in arithmetic had finished. The Rev. Selby Ord, at the close of the day's work, asked the neutral ministers to address the schoolmaster and scholars. They complimented both on the highly satisfactory state of the school. They were in good humour, with the school, the visitors, and themselves, and were in expectation of a good dinner at the manse. The scholars were glad to be free. The dinner party wended their way to the manse, where Jenny Chapman was in a flutter of excitement, though she had an extra hand to help her. Everything went off well. The drivers of the carts dined in the kitchen. The robin was also a guest, and hopped about and chirped its song as a welcome to the visitors. It went into the back kitchen, where was the water pump, and in the mouth of the pipe it found for itself a supply of water, where it drank and was filled. When the roast was set on the dinner table, it perched itself on top of it, and a weather-beaten man named Sandy Gillie [6], who was at the point of using knife and fork suddenly dropped them, and at the same time exclaimed, in an earnest voice, *"Is this hoose canny ?"*

Many years passed away. The Edgars and the Guilds of the school days grew to be men and women. They dropped away from the Lammermuirs, and found homes in distant parts of the earth. The wide Atlantic rolled its many hundreds of miles of waves between the Guilds and the Edgars in the old country, but in the silent watches of the day and night, the sight of the rippling lake at Dirrington, and the purple heather on its sides, often came to them as a reality, and they sometimes felt they were again at the Dairy Well on the Law, drinking its cool, sparkling water after their scrambles and sports in the warm autumn days of their youth, and they often thought that no nectar like that water would ever enter their lips in the years to come.

Dirrington Law (Sketch)

Notes - Glimpse VI

1. **Alexander Wilson**, Paisley poet. (1766-1813). Alexander Wilson was born in Paisley where he worked as a weaver and later as a travelling packman. His first verses were published in 1790 and when "Watty and Meg" came out, many people thought it had been written by Robert Burns. He was imprisoned for a while in Paisley for satirising a local dignitary. On his release he went to the United States. After tackling a variety of jobs he embarked on a major study of American birds. He travelled extensively and produced in 1804 "The American Ornithology" which established his reputation among his new countrymen. He died in Philadelphia in 1813 from dysentery brought on by his exertions.

2. **James Fortune.** (1813- 1893). Married Janet Wilson in 1837. His wife died in 1886. He worked as a drainer with his son John who died in 1911 at the age of 68. His daughter, Isabella, died in 1931 at the age of 90.

3. **Fasten's E'en.** This was the day before the start of Lent - the Scots equivalent of Shrove Tuesday.

4. **Handsel Monday.** This was the first Monday after the Scottish New Year. It was traditionally a day of holiday when farmers would pay their labourers their wages. It was also a day for staying in bed late; for it was widely believed that this was the day the fairies were about until the morning.

5. **Cockfighting.** Cockfighting was an ancient tradition carried out on Fasten's E'en in schools all over Scotland. A holiday was given to the children who had to pay the schoolmaster a fee to enter a cock which should have been home bred. A ring was formed in the school-room and the birds kept covered until it was their turn to fight. The cock that gained the most victories or that 'keepit the fleer langist' was named 'King'. The owner of the winning cock bore the title of 'King' for a year. The fees collected were a useful supplement to the schoolmaster's

meagre salary and the dead or disabled cocks made a welcome addition to his diet. The practice did not die out in many places in Scotland until well into the 19th century, a reminder perhaps that the moral outlook of our ancestors was very different from our own.

6. **Sandy Gillie**. Alexander Gillie herd in Cranshaws. His wife was Martha Bruce whom he married in 1777 at Cranshaws when they were rebuked for getting married irregularly. They had five children; Elizabeth - who married George Bruce (Thus making Sandy Gillie my g.-g.-g.-g.-grandfather. Editor), Elspeth, George, James and Agnes. Alexander Gillie died in 1824.

Bridge over the Dye

Glimpse VII.

It was a bright and mild afternoon towards the end of March. The sky was a pale blue interspersed with light fleecy clouds, and overhead it seemed like a palpable dome. The trees by the river and round the church and churchyard were well defined against the distant horizon, and looked like the beautiful workmanship of skilled hands. The thin leafless branches were like the fine tracery of a drawing. Overhead the rooks that had wintered at the Peely Wood, by the banks of the Whitadder had returned to their old haunts, and were busy at the work of nest building, and as their homes progressed, they rejoiced over the task by cawing incessantly. A crescent moon, pale and high in the sky, looked down from the south-east. The river was well filled with brown water, which hurried on gladly, as if under the influence of fine weather. Primroses dotted its banks, and looked slyly from the thick grass of the fields. The crocus was rich, and contrasted well with the polished green of the shrubbery. Birds hopped about and chirped their spring notes, and settled upon the quiet corners for their annual nests; while the lark on Whitchester heights enlivened the woodman near with its clear and cheery notes.

At the door, and smoking his pipe, at the upper part of the village stood George Symington[1], shoemaker, with his bald bare head, his round foot, and leather apron. His keen black eyes took in the scene as he gazed around, and being a naturalist, he watched closely the feathered race at work. Inside, round his window, and near his seat in the workshop, hung a few cages with canaries and bullfinches, and judging from their chirping, whistling, and lively pranks they were cutting on the tiny spars, they too felt the power of a genial spring. In the evening the shoemaker was again on his stool, and, with the aid of a yellow light from a soft thick tallow candle in a long wooden candlestick, placed in such a position as to enable him to accomplish the "closing" of "uppers" for a pair of stout boots, he held the "clawms"[2] firmly between his knees, applied the awl to the leather, inserted the "birse"[3], and pulled the "lingens"[4] smartly and tightly to effect a compact union of the leathers. The shop was small, but, in addition to himself, it held half-a-dozen men and boys, who had gradually dropped in from the villages and farms on business, or gossip, or rest.

They went over a pretty substantial field of gossip, connected with their own and other parishes, and not a few sly hits were aimed at absent individuals, which caused laughter and merriment. But all were sober-minded, when a startling piece of news was related by George Bruce [5] from Kippetlaw. He gave it as it had been told to him sometime before in Dunse. As Wattie Cossar, [6] a well-known horse dealer, was crossing the hills on horseback on his return journey from Hallow Fair, he came upon a gig and two men in it, just at the top of Hardens Hill. The time of night and the appearance of the party aroused his suspicions, and he forcibly stopped their progress. The two men, alarmed at the active and strong horseman, left the gig, and fled into the moor and escaped. Cossar tied his horse to the gig, jumped into it, and drove on to Dunse. As a dead body had been found in the gig, the people of the town turned out in great excitement and rage, and were not pacified until the conveyance had been burnt. The dead body was taken back to Edrom Churchyard, where it had been extracted[7]. The idlers in the shoemaker's shop stole quietly and quickly home, and cast as they went fearful glances through the gloom of night. Even George Bruce, as he stepped smartly through the heather path on his way homewards, was not equal to his former courage of relating the story, but the faithful company of his black-and-tan collie was great consolation to him, and when a light appeared in the window at the back of his cottage, he felt decided relief.

The morning ushered in the humour of "Gowk's Day,"[8] and the last month of spring. Then hope is strong in man and nature, when the genial western breezes unfold the buds and flowers, when the swallows skimming the river valley are welcome, and when the notes of the cuckoo arrest the footsteps of the shepherd on the height, and the ploughman at his sowing if the season be late. As George Symington was at the preparations of the lasts for the ploughman's new boots, the uppers of which he had finished the previous night, a boy with red hair and freckled face appeared, and said that Bob Currie had sent him with a cup to get a pennyworth of "*doo's mIlk*." The shoemaker took in the situation at a glance, and said he was sorry his pigeons were not giving any milk at present, but if he went over to the mill he would be sure to get the article. Willie Sharp had employed another boy to go to George Sherriff's the schoolmaster, to say that he would be obliged by giving him the loan of the history of Adam's Grandfather. When the fun had gone so far it was discovered; but a smart little girl, when she had an opportunity, looked into the master's face, and very innocently said, "*Your shoe's buckle is loose, sir.*" This brought laughter to the little assembly, in which the worthy schoolmaster joined.

As the forenoon advanced the scholars became fidgety, and it was rumoured that the fox-hounds were to meet that morning at the village. According to custom, the school was dismissed, and the children hurried down to the village to see the coming of the hounds, and the horsemen from the town of Dunse, and under the superintendence of young Mr Hay of Dunse Castle, who acted as master of the hounds and huntsman in one. Already some farmers had ridden quietly in, and were at the door of the Inn, where Nancy Mickle, the landlord's daughter, was serving them with ale, and a stronger potion which might have come from the still in the valley of Kilmaid, for they praised its quality and flavour, and joked about the Kilmaid burn having a peaty taste. As Nancy had been surprised by the horses' hoofs and the talking of the riders, just as she was examining a valentine drawn cautiously from a private drawer, and which she had received last St. Valentine's Day, and which contained some fat-winged cupids with bows and arrows aimed at a couple walking up an avenue to a distant church, she did not appear at the door without a tinge of a monthly rose on her pleasant face.

At length the red coats came smartly down the hill and turned down the avenue by the church to the "Big House," where Robert Hall had refreshments for them. The dogs were swinging their great tails in the air, and their stolid, dogged faces indicated that they knew the work on which they were bent. A meet in the hills was refreshing to the keen sportsman, and came like the last bite of the season. The fields in the Merse forbade such late sport. The village folk were as excited over it as the lower animals, for Smoutie in its stable had been hammering with its feet all the morning, as if news of their coming had been sent to it. Some of the villagers hurried up to the high ground at the Dimples, and some to the top of Craigie, to have a good view of the field and the run. But although the Manse offered a wide and open view, it was often remarked that the Rev. Selby Ord was never seen to countenance this sport. He sometimes thought that if the hunters could fancy themselves in the position of the fox, with scores of animals behind them intent on their death, they would be inclined to leave the field and wander home. The hounds were thrown into Craigie Covert, and in a twinkling their music was heard over the hillside. The fox doubled on Horseupcleugh, made for Cranshaws Castle and the Innerwick Road, and was eventually lost. Tom Sherriff, like many more, was following on foot, but he pursued his walk to Trottenshaw and Byrecleugh to visit his fellow-student, John Usher[9], who was now home to the solitude and sentiment of his beloved glen. The Dye was glittering in the sunshine like a piece of frosted silver. Here and there old twisted birch trees bordered the path, over which tiny hill burns crossed and sang as they went to join the river. In some fields sheep were fenced in by nets, and were cleaning up the last crop of turnips. Away in the distance, among the rounded peaks of the hills, smoke was rising from the annual burning of the overgrown heather, but where the sky was not obscured, it showed a light blue. A stiff refreshing breeze blew down the glen, taking as it were Tom Sherriff by the throat. The linties were making a concert above the singing stream, which was spanned here and there by a rustic bridge. Soon Dye Cottage with its background of sheltering trees, and Trottenshaw with its flat-roofed outhouses, appeared as Tom stepped smartly around the curve of the road. In a field adjoining the river Tom came upon Geordie Johnston[10] ploughing with a team of oxen, which were making high ridges and deep furrows all over the height. The honest fellow rested the patient, tractable animals, and chatted with the youth on the brae, where the primroses were peeping from the thick mossy grass. At Tom's request Geordie, proud of the stock, counted on his fingers the following eight animals, naming them as he counted: There were - (1) Willie Weel; (2) Kippie Shiel; (3) Budgieman; (4) Body; (5) Leatherman; (6) Laughter; (7) Scanty Creesh; (8) Toddy. Then the ploughman urged on his ousen[11] to their task, and young Sherriff resumed his walk towards Byrecleugh, to which place a pretty piece of river lies before the wayfarer. It is bordered on each side with heights clothed with mossy grass and heather, and the rippling stream sometimes twists itself round rocky corners and murmurs over its rocky bed, and forever makes pleasant music as it goes. Here and there may be seen what the shepherds call a "stell." This is a circular enclosure built of dry stone, about five feet high, and the stones are so compact that they resemble in their outer surface the ends of baker's rolls one piled upon the other. An entrance leads into this "stell," and there the sheep are driven for shelter during a severe snowstorm. Byrecleugh, snugly situated in a little bay, so to speak, among the hills, soon burst upon his view, and he now saw the shooting-lodge of the Duke of Roxburghe, with its quaint roof thatched with heather and the comfortable cottages and stable at its side, under the shade of the old ash and elm trees, and in front the fresh grassy meadow running down to the river which glittered in the sunshine. On the opposite side of the stream might be seen the ruin of a house called Handaxewood, where the accomplished and eccentric Sir George Home of Wedderburn[12] had built ages ago a hunting-house, where he might amuse himself in the training of horses and in falconry.

Tom Sherriff had now met his friend John Usher, and they interchanged thoughts on this wayward baronet, and imagined him galloping up and down the road in the solitary glen in the moonlight for his recreation. They saw him go out with his hawks to the hillside, and heard the tinkling of their silver bells. Thomas Usher[13], the manager of the Duke's hill property, gave Tom a hearty welcome, and, after a rest, the two students wandered up the hill, away from the river for about a quarter of a mile, to see the "Mutiny Stones"[14]. These two youths had much in common. The spirit of poetry was welling up in both their natures, and the thirst for knowledge kept their minds at work. Although they loved the hills and glens and rivers of their nativity, after their sojourn in the capital, the power of human life had seized upon their natures, and at times, the remembrance of their winter activity made them ill at ease among moorland solitudes. Now, they came upon an enormous heap of stones, which had lain for centuries, and no man to this day can give a satisfactory theory of their origin. Tom Sherriff paced their length, and he found it to be about one hundred yards, and the height appeared to be from ten to fifteen feet. Learned men, and men skilled in the customs of olden times, had come to see them, and have left the mystery behind them. The old inhabitants of the moorlands called them the "Mittenfu' Stanes," and, standing on them as the students now did, they saw Dirrington Law in the distance, looking over the undulating uplands as if to guard them. The sky here and there behind the high ground was obscured with columns of smoke from the burning heather, and to a lively imagination this did not fail to resemble the smoke from the cannon in the field of battle. But, as Tom's father was still full of the Spanish War, this might account for the ready resemblance. The silence around was overwhelming. The cry of the whaup and the peewit and the distant murmur of the Dye only broke the stillness, and down the cleugh to the left of the lodge, the tiny burn called the Byre tinkled over its rocky descent and prattled to the stray birch trees as it hurried to its end. As the two sat on the moss-covered stones, the following legend, which hangs about the Lammermuirs as to the origin of the "Mittenfu' Stanes," was related by young Usher:- The devil had been employed to make a cauld on the Tweed at Kelso, and as it required an enormous quantity of stones to carry out the work, he crossed the Lammermuirs to the sea-coast at Dunbar and carried them on his back, and on some heavy journeys he stowed them carefully away about his person, and flew o'er the hilltops to his destination. In one of his journeys the night was dark, and there was no sign of moon or stars, and through the murky air he sped resolutely on his way; but miscalculating the position of one of the heights, he grazed one of his hands on the whinstone hillside, and thinking no more of this little accident, he reached a point above Byrecleugh, when his "mitten" burst and down fell its contents, which to this day are called the "Mittenfu' Stanes." John Usher continued, and said that it was believed by folk in the moorlands that underneath this pile of stones the hide of an ox, filled with gold pieces had been buried, and if anyone had the courage to dig for it, the gold would be found there. Again, he pointed his finger to a glen adjoining the Dyeside, but situated on a burn named the Kirsten, which joins the Dye. Here within sound of the stream, and sheltered by the Cleugh, and adorned by a few rowan trees, which gave out sweet perfume in summer and red berries in autumn, stood a small cottage, kept as an inn by Kirsty Cleugh. In far-off times the monks, in their pilgrimage across the moor from Dunbar to Melrose, and from Melrose to Dunbar, halted at the inn and refreshed themselves with a stoup of ale, or, maybe, a glass of smuggled whisky, for the monks, as all the world knows, were men who enjoyed good fare. In the hot days of summer they spent a day or two, and sometimes they might be seen cooling or washing their feet in the rippling water, while others went a-fishing to provide for themselves a savoury repast. In later times, a worthy divine from a Merse town rode up and held a gathering on the haugh in the long summer Sunday evenings, and from hill and glen in Lauderdale and Lammermuir, shepherd and ploughman assembled to hear the words of this evangelical speaker. Even hollows and sheltered places were pointed out as the abodes of those who were persecuted when the royal troops scoured the country, to arrest by force the high-minded and self-sacrificing Covenanters[16].

It was growing dusk when Tom Sherriff left the moorland road and came down upon the manse. He met Jenny Chapman coming out of the out-houses where she had been securing the poultry for the night, for, said she, these "rampagin" foxes were out on the poaching when one least expected them. Jenny was a careful and thrifty housekeeper to the minister, and treated her animals as if they were her friends. The smell of burning thorns and the cleaning of gardens was in the air, for the villagers had been making preparations for the planting and sowing of spring. He met Mr Ord coming up the hill, and in the midst of casual remarks, he told him to come up to the manse soon, and he would show him the last new volume of poems of his old friend Wordsworth, whom he knew when he resided among the Cumberland Hills. Wordsworth, he said, had a love for inanimate nature, and his theory that this nature was sentient to him and others, especially in solitude, a most consoling philosophy. When Tom reached the schoolhouse he found his father and Jamie Wilson,[17] the miller, absorbed in a game of draughts, and they were speechless over the "dam-bord." His mother-canny body- gave him the key to the situation, and, as the schoolmaster had just lost one of his crowned men, he sat down at the glowing fire, and soon was half asleep, after the long and bracing walk among the hills.

Longformacus House (Sketch)

Notes - Glimpse VII

1. **George Symington.** Born c.1801. His wife's maiden name was Hannah.

2. **'clawms'.** Shoemaker's last or clamp.

3. **'birse'.** Bristles fixed on end of a shoemaker's thread.

4. **'lingens'.** Waxed thread used by shoemakers.

5. **George Bruce.** He married Elizabeth Gillie, daughter of Alexander Gillie at Cranshaws in 1784. Their children were: Peter b.1787, Alexander b.1789, James b.1791 all in Cranshaws and Allison b.1793, Ann b.1798, George b.1803, Martha b.1805 and Agnes b.1806, all in Longformacus. (His daughter, Ann, was the mother of my great-grandmother; thus making George Bruce my g.-g.-.g.-grandfather. Ed.).

6. **Wattie Cosser.** (1785-1839). Horse dealer in Duns. His grand-father, Walter Cosser, was also a horse dealer who died in 1776. His father, who was also called Walter and carried on the traditional family occupation. He married Isabella Cockburn who died in 1861 at the age of 77. They had eight children but none of them were called 'Walter'.

7. **Resurrectionists or Body Snatchers**. Throughout the 18th century and the early years of the 19th, when scientific medicine was in its infancy, there was a great shortage of bodies available for dissection and study of human anatomy. Surgeons were allowed to use the bodies of people who died in correction houses, foundlings, suicides and those who were condemned to death by a magistrate. But demand was always ahead of supply. An illicit trade grew up in digging up fresh graves and selling the bodies to surgeons. The Scots Presbyterian looked forward to the day when the last trump would sound and the graves would open up for the dead to face the last judgement. The activities of the grave-robbers were thus regarded with alarm and revulsion by many who thought their loved ones would not be there when the trump was sounded. The activities of Burke and Hare in Edinburgh in the late 1820's, though technically they were not grave-robbers, only served to

heighten the hysteria surrounding the activities of the body-snatchers.

[8]. **Gowk's Day.** The equivalent of April Fool's day. 'Gowk' was the Scots name for the cuckoo whose arrival heralded the start of spring. To send someone on a 'gowk's errand' owes its origins to the speed and secrecy with which a gowk could move through the undergrowth. The cry of the gowk would be heard coming from one spot, but when the searcher reached there he would hear the cry coming from another spot - and so it went on.

[9]. **John Usher.** Son of Thomas Usher (see below). He was born in 1810. In 1825 he went to Edinburgh University with the intention of training for the ministry. He was highly regarded for his poetry. In 1829 he returned home on a snowy winter's day, caught cold and died after a few hours' illness. He is buried in Melrose Churchyard.

[10]. **George Johnston.** (1779-1860). Had farmed in Midlothian and in Selkirk, died at Rulemains, Duns.

[11]. **'Ousen'.** Scots for 'oxen'.

[12]. **Sir George Home of Wedderburn.** Son of Sir David Home of Wedderburn and brother to the historian David Home of Godscroft. He was born circa 1560.

[13]. **Thomas Usher.** Born in 1784, in the 1841 Census a Thomas Usher is described as being an agricultural labourer in Byrecleugh. He was aged 57 and was living with his wife, Helen Ewart, and children; Robert, Thomas, Charles and Jane.

[14]. **Mittenfu' or Mutiny Stones.** The Stones are actually Stone and Bronze Age burial cairns. Bodies were buried whole or partially cremated and the remains placed in urns over which were built huge cairns of stones.

[15]. **Covenanters.** The enforcement of rights of patronage and the introduction of a form of episcopalianism into the Church of Scotland led to 262 ministers being 'deprived' of their livings in 1663. The ousted ministers were still held in high regard by their parishioners and continued to conduct services outdoors. In the 1670's increasingly harsh laws were passed against unlicensed ministers and their congregations. Conventicles were held in remote places despite the fact that any clergyman who presided over such a gathering could face the death penalty. The Covenanting movement was particularly strong in the

south-west of Scotland though a number of conventicles were held in Berwickshire in the 1670's. Among a list of suspected Covenanters were: Margaret Fortune of Crenshes, Margaret Tunnock in Raeburn. Sir Robert Sinclair of Longformacus was sympathetic to the Covenanting movement and the ousted minister of the parish of Westruther, William Veitch, was to become one of the heroes of the movement.

[16]. **Jamie Wilson.** His wife was Janet Mack who died in 1842 at the age of sixty-five. They were married in 1808 in Longformacus.

Curling Rink (Sketch)

Twinlaw Cairns

Glimpse VIII

The world is made up of contrasts, and light and shadow lie close together from the cradle to the grave. Along the path of life, the comic and the tragic muse pipe their tunes within each other's hearing. And so pondered David White[1], schoolmaster of Drinkwell, tall, bent, and closely shaven, with firmly closed lips, and a lowering brow, as he paced up and down his garden overlooking the old churchyard on this warm evening in May, when the blossom was decorating his apple and cherry trees, and the foliage in Murray Street was green and fresh, and fluttering over the newly-made grave which the aged sexton had just prepared for the morrow. The little avenues leading to the open space of ground at the foot of the churchyard were in a brisk state with boys and girls, young men and maidens, and those advanced in life, and the various roads leading into the town were dotted with groups of people hurrying in on some pleasant errand, judging from their gait and jocularity; and even in the streets the apprentices rattled on their shutters with swifter alacrity than was their want. Before long the crowd was formed into a ring, with the aid of poles and ropes to keep it in its place. Inside the arena the clown, in his paint, tights and cap, was cracking jokes with the acrobat, and it might seem to one unaccustomed to their ways of life, say to Davie Wilson[2] at Edrom, that they were the happiest beings in creation. Looking round, the schoolmaster, who was keeping his eye on the doings, thought he had never seen such a large turn-out at any circus performance. As John Delaney, tall and muscular, and lithe, was turning somersaults on the spring-board, and mounting a ladder held by his own hands, and the clown was caricaturing him by turns, room was made for an equestrian to enter the ring with his black mare - called "Black Bess." This was an old man dressed like a countryman, and the clown jeered and laughed at the idea of such an old stiff fellow being able to mount and manage such a swift-footed steed. However, he was helped to get upon its back, and in a few minutes he was standing there, and the steed was careering round the ring, as if it enjoyed and knew every movement of its rider. Thomas Ord[3], for that was the name of the circus horseman, peered round at the onlookers, who stood in great numbers all round the circle, and he once or twice fixed his eyes in quarters where he recognised a well-known face, such as that of William Bertram[4], farmer, Cranshaws, for it was market-day at Drinkwell, but these only spurred him on to do his very best in this character performance. The old yeoman was soon turned into Dick Turpin by the drawing of a cord, and the falling of some outer garments and the exchanging of a hat, in his famous ride to York; then this took the place of William Tell in the same way, with his bow and arrow, and the expertness in their use when he cut the apple in two on his own boy's head; then this was exchanged for the sailor boy, which in its turn became Rob Roy. As one character succeeded another he was loudly cheered by the spectators, and then the well-behaved and intelligent horse seemed from the glitter of its eye to enjoy the prevailing enthusiasm. After this, as the famous equestrian was going the rounds of the circus, one or two persons rather forward in their inquiries as to his identity, and seeking to ingratiate themselves into his favour, made some advances on him, but they were coldly but politely set aside, and he was not molested again.

Standing together were Tom Sherriff and others who had walked from the Lammermuirs to see one whom they knew to be intimately associated with the district. It had been his father's wish for him to go and spy the land when the travelling showman appeared. As David White had invited Tom to supper, and as the evening was advancing, he left the crowd, and when he entered the schoolhouse he found the schoolmaster in his own kitchen in his white shirt sleeves busy cooking some trout he had just caught that morning in the Blackadder, on the Nisbet grounds. David White was gruff, and scowling, and pedantic, but he was hospitable and sociable, and a good liver, and so particular was he about the cooking of some articles of diet, that he would occasionally be seen over the kitchen fire with a knife and fork in hand, turning the article in the pan to suit his particular taste, as he was seen to-night. His lips were closely pressed, and his mouth was pursed out, and he turned the frizzling fish as if they refused to be cooked according to his mind. The supper was served in his sitting-room, which was well supplied with some fine old engravings and a well-filled bookcase, where his favourite Virgil, Dante, and Pope reposed, and were ready at hand. His wife was a little, thin woman, with a pale washed-out complexion, and she quietly sat at table and heard her lord throwing lines of the great classics at the head of Tom, as if he had been a Bedlington terrier worrying a cat. They had no family. Some said that his bark was worse than his bite, but those who had attended his school would sometimes answer that his bite was far worse than his bark. Supper being ended and time moving on, Tom prepared for his homeward journey; but as they crossed the square, the schoolmaster took him into the bar of the White Swan Hotel, which was only set apart for a select few, and there he refreshed him with a glass of his favourite claret. When they were parting he flung at him a couplet of Pope, and told him to get on with his studies, for said he, "*I have never found that a little learning is a dangerous thing,*" and "*I know half a loaf is better than no bread.*" Then Tom picked up some of his hill cronies and hurried home. The walk was uphill and long, and they were all much fatigued before they reached the "Strips," and were glad when they came within sound of the brawling river running through the still night.

About noon of the following day, during the interval of the dinner hour, a group of villagers hung on the bridge, and mixed their resting-time with a strong dose of gossip, among which was the news of the circus at Drinkwell, and especially the appearance of the son of their minister as a clever and fearless equestrian. The different tradesmen were well represented, and others who were employed by Laird Hume in the woods and those on the farms. The laird had now returned from Inveresk; and it had been rumoured that as some of his men on different occasions, in going across the country, had become the worse of drink, he had written to say that " the lad Mack was to come over, as he always did well." So the lad Mack brought him over. As the loungers were in the midst of their talk, Tom Sherriff appeared with his dog Dye, and he was accosted and surrounded for information about Thomas Ord whose father had lately passed up the hill, when they very respectfully lifted their caps and looked inquiringly at him. Tom had his fishing-rod and basket, and was on his way for a little excursion to hill and glen, for he meant to climb the Twinlaws and see the cairns, and return by the valley of the Watch. In going, he took the road to Rawburn, and then cut across the moor until he came within sight of the Scarlaws. He then mounted the hill on the south-east side. He had never before been on top of the Twinlaws, and as he had heard much about the cairns erected there in ages past, his curiosity was stirred to see and learn about them. As he gradually ascended, a wide and extensive country burst upon his view. It was fortunate for him that he met a shepherd called Tammy Dyat [5] on the hillside, attending to the duties of the lambing season. He got his company a considerable way up the hill, and he arranged to meet him again on his return. At one time Tammy's son had wandered among the hills and was nearly lost, but they found him a great distance from home, and on the way to Lauder.

Tom and Dye were ready for a rest, as the trudging through the wet grass and heather had taken the stamina from them. Indeed, Dye became so worn out on several occasions that his master had to lift him and carry him in his arms, lest as he thought his heart would burst. A big hare burst away from its haunts among the grass near the top, but Dye was too fatigued to try his short legs in a forlorn chase. When Tom reached the flat top of the hill, the strange and old world look of the cairns, and the expansive panorama of landscape, were like to take his breath away. He sat and rested in the little recess on the east side of the south cairn. He felt very lonely sitting there, and the immense extent of country reaching from the sea on the east coast of the county to Berwick, the Cheviots and Eildon Hills, and round on the peaks of the Lammermuirs with villages, and farms, and plantations, blurred in the hundreds of miles of cultivated land, moorland and hills, did not lessen the feelings of solitude and isolation which came over him.

The hill reaches the height of 1466 feet above the level of the sea, and the cairns stand at a distance from each other of about 60 yards. The foundation of each cairn consists of a mound of stones gradually rising on all sides to a height of about 6 feet, and on this base stands the cairn or monument shaped somewhat like a long cask about 12 feet or 14 feet high, and built compactly of undressed stones. At the sides at intervals stones jut out to allow one to ascend to the top, which has a small hollow for standing room. Rain, snow, and wind have no noticeable influence over these structures, although they have stood through centuries. Among the conspicuous objects which Tom singled out were Hume Castle, and the Big and Little Dirringtons lay below not unlike the shape of big dogs at rest, and it was pleasant to see the green fields at Scarlaw and the Watch winding down its deep glen. But the feeling of loneliness increased to such a degree that Tom was glad to pursue his downward path. He again met a hill man named John Lillie, who told him that no man knew the origin and history of these monuments. He said a legend goes the round that a chief had two sons who took different sides in a war between England and Scotland - one went into the English army, and the other stuck to his father in the Scotch army. A time came for a close engagement, the two sons met as opponents, and they were slain by each other's hand. The aged father recognised his sons and mourned for their fate. But to commemorate this event, and raise a memorial to the two brothers, the soldiers agreed to erect the cairns. Accordingly they drew themselves up into a line reaching from the hill top to the river Watch, and stone after stone was handed along the line until they had collected a sufficient quantity for the work. [6]

When Tom and John Lillie and Tommy Dyat arrived at the march between Byrecleugh and Scarlaw, Lillie put his crook on a piece of heather and told Tom that underneath there rested the body of a labourer who lived at Scarlaw, and who took away his own life, and according to an old custom, he was buried apart. This poor man had discovered that the sunny side of his years had passed, and that for him the gloom of his coming years must be ended. In looking more closely at the heather, Tom found the nest of a muirfowl with eggs in it on top of the grave, so that in the midst of death there was life.

At Twinlawford in the house of John Hudson[7], Tom rested before he began his fishing, which promised to be favourable, as the Watch was in good order after the rain which had fallen a few days previously. The Watch is a bonnie stream, and has some fine currents as they enter and leave the deep pools which are to be found along its course in this pastoral and sheltered vale. Tom, like all the hill boys, had learned the art of fishing when he was hardly able to hold the rod, and catching trout came to him like a part of his being. Wandering along the side of the

prattling stream and picking out the pretty speckled trout, he gradually
came to a point where it leaves the open and flows down a glen clothed
on both sides with woods. Here he left it; and as the evening was
enticing and a real fishing one, he dropped down upon the Dye at
Fosterside, which stood on the right bank of the river, a little above the
scaurs. There was a rustic bridge here which was convenient for those
going up the hill towards the Manse, or for those going on business to
Cranshaws, for Rawburn and the other farms were a detached part of
that parish. Tom began a few successful casts here, but his attention was
soon taken up by the appearance of a tall, slender man dressed in a cloak
and slouched hat. He came smartly up the side of the river, and walked
quickly over the bridge and disappeared up the hill at the top of Craigie,
about the old wall adjoining the Manse garden. Tom thought he had
seen this person before, and as he came down to the open side of green
pasture or glade on the side of the Dye opposite Craigie, he was
surprised to meet a man and a boy with a trap, whose horse had been
taken out and was quietly feeding there. He recognised this man as John
Delaney of the circus, with his long, black, wavy hair. He was putting up
his fishing rod, and he gave Tom no encouragement to come nearer him.
So young Sherriff went on his way, and pondered these things in his
heart.

The blossom of the rowan tree was out, and its scent filled the close
evening air. People remembered months after that this blossom came to
a rich perfection in the form of red berries, for in the month of November
the branches overhanging the brae sides seemed as if they had been
tipped with blood, so red and fresh and beautiful was their contrast with
the blackness proverbial to this month. The river here makes a splendid
turn like a bent elbow, and there is a deep pool called the Heron's hole,
and a little further down, as it were at the fingers of the arm, it goes
whirling round a wild rocky corner, tossing itself into foam. In the
distance one can see the round top of Dirrington Law, and the high
ground towards Otterburn, while the open space below Craigie has a
pleasant pastoral look dotted with its cattle and sheep. At the left side of
the river, on high rocky ground, stood what people now call the
foundations of Craigie Castle. On a bright summer day, when it was
inhabited and the windows were open to admit the sweet air and the

sound of the stream, a maid in charge of a little girl dandled it in her arms over the castle wall. The child was so pleased with the exercise that it made a sudden jerk and fell from the nurse's arms into the pool below and was drowned.

In the meantime the person in the slouched hat, whom Tom Sherriff had seen, had made his way to the entrance of the manse, and as the farmer of Fosterside had been on a visit to the Rev. Selby Ord about the baptisement of his child, he encountered him. He had been telling the minister how his house was situated with regard to the dangerous proximity to these fearful reptiles, the moorland adders. He said that they had become so common that they sometimes found them in the house, and if they could not get rid of them he and his family would have to leave the place. The farmer hid behind a tree and watched the movements of the stranger. The latter, seeing a light in an upstairs window, went forward cautiously, picked up a few pebbles from the walk and threw them gently on the window and waited the result. When this was done a second time, the minister looked out, withdrew without making a sign or speaking a word, came downstairs, opened the door, and beckoned the stranger to enter. He did so, and both went quietly into his study. Jenny Chapman was in the kitchen at this time, poring over a volume of Harvey's *"Contemplations on the Starry Heavens,"* and so engrossed was she with the showy garniture of the verbiage with which the author clothes his style, that she heard no sound of anything unusual. When it became time for her to retire, she was attracted by the sound of voices in the study, and wondering who the visitor could be, she, although not an eavesdropper, put her ear to the door and listened. There was no mistake but that there was a second person, and the two were in earnest conversation. The one whose voice was not familiar to her was pleading in a manly way for the good name of his occupation. He said that people spoke slightingly of it, not from their own knowledge of it, but from hearsay. It was just this, *"Give a dog a bad name, and hang it."* It gave him great delight to see the weary and heavy laden of this world enjoying their entertainment, and forgetting for a brief season in their distraction their earthly cares. Jenny retired to the shelter of an adjoining room at this stage, and waited cautiously. After a little time she again listened, and now only one voice was heard. It was that of the minister, and he was at prayer. The night was well advanced when the two came out. Jenny peered through the half-closed door, and then went to the front window, where she saw the minister in front of the manse bid his son farewell. The latter bounded away down the hill towards the river, and as he disappeared in the twilight of a summer night, he looked round and waved his hand to his father, who waved his in turn.

Those who knew young Ord at this time, and in his old age, and compared him with his father, remarked how like unto him he became. He had the same tall, wiry figure, the same grey eye, the same wrinkled and somewhat reserved face, and the same wavy, grey hair. Many yet can recall the well-known equestrian, as he appeared on the Sundays on his tours, with the big Bible under his arm, and accompanied by his family, he reverently sat in the pew of the Parish Kirk. Perhaps at those times his memory went back to the old home in Lammermuir, and the scenes he was never to visit again. They also remembered the careful attention to the education of his children, as he lost no opportunity of improving their minds, for he sent them to the parish school wherever he went, and there they picked up the crumbs of learning from the liberal minds of the old type of schoolmasters, whose lives and work were not an unimportant lever to lift their country into its present scale of civilisation and prosperity.

Notes - Glimpse VIII -

1. **David White,** schoolmaster in Duns. (1761-1822). His wife was Mary Johnston who died in 1798 at the age of 45. They had a son, William, who died in Virginia in 1814 at the age of 34.

2. **Davie Wilson** of Edrom. Married Jane Landels at Edrom in 1854.

3. **Thomas Ord.** (1800-1864). The son of the Rev. Selby Ord who upset his father by giving up a professional career and joining the circus. He was a very accomplished equestrian who was well known throughout the Lothians and Borders. In his middle-age he was described as " a tall manly-looking man - a strong clean-shaven face who was always well dressed." He died in Biggar and ironically, his Death Certificate states that his parents were 'unknown'.

4. **William Bertram,** farmer, Cranshaws. (1807-1843). His wife was Anne Taylor (1831-1898). Their son, John Scott Bertram (1831-1895) was also a tenant in Cranshaws

5. **Tammy Dyat.** In the Cranshaws .Parish .Register it is noted that in 1814 Thomas Dyat of Dunside House had a son George. Two years later his twin sons Thomas and David were born. He is described as a shepherd in these records. In 1818 the Cranshaws Kirk Sessions supplied Thomas Dyet with oatmeal for his family. In 1826 they gave him 2/- out of the Poor Funds. Times were obviously hard for Thomas Dyat.

6. **Twinlaw Cairns.** The legend also says that the two brothers were Edgars of Wedderlie. It was not uncommon for our ancestors to erect cairns to mark a place where some momentous event had occurred.

7. **John Hudson.** (1780-1853). His wife was Jennet Ford (1775-1850). They had a son, John who died in 1893 at the age of 60.

The Schoolhouse

Glimpse IX

Society hangs together like a string of beads, some of which have a greater brilliancy and value than their less showy and modest comrades, but all join in unity to carry out their purpose of ornament and use. The beads of the town are more numerous and varied than those of the country, but as the country ones are fewer, they consequently become more valuable. In this way the essential craftsmen of a village hang on the string in a very prominent position. They are the blacksmith, the tailor, and the shoemaker, and these workers may construct with their materials of iron, wood, cloth, leather, a network of such strength as to encompass much good or evil in a rural community. Day and night, and the wants of man are on their side, for customers and idlers from all corners of the parish assemble in their workshops, which to the village become clubs, news rooms, and debating societies. This pertains more in winter than in summer, as weather and out-door occupations to some extent break up the customs of the long winter nights. And so it was on this warm evening in July. The ringing of the hammer on anvil, the rasp of the saw, and the thud of the loom were laid aside for garden work or neighbourly conversation. The beating of the leather of the shoemaker was exchanged for the setting up of his early potatoes, and the tailor had released his needle from the sewing of button holes for the management of his bees. At their doorsteps dames sat and knitted their stockings, and their wheels were laid aside for the day. Boys and girls chased each other at their games round the remains of last year's peat stacks, for the new stock was not yet laid in. By the river side and in the river they played, and waded in the stream, and caught trouts under the stones with their hands. George Sherriff had his hands full in his little glebe, for, after the school work, he had set himself to make his own hay, the crop was long and thick, and full of good clover, and the exercise of the scythe brought the sweat from one not too accustomed to manual labour. But a few of the villagers lounged into the field, and very considerately gave him a help, and in this way his task was lightened. As the evening wore away, all signs of labour began to cease, and the women who had been acting as milk-maids in the pasture fields, brought home their pitchers full of foaming milk.

A party of gypsies were seen to come down the hill and cross the bridge, and halt opposite the inn. They consisted of a dark swarthy man and his black-eyed wife, his daughter browned by the sun and two children. Henry Niel[1] who had just come up from the smithy, fell into conversation with them, and the other villagers sitting outside the inn on a wooden seat, called out jokingly to Henry to have his fortune read by the gypsy girl. Henry Niel belonged to a family whose name it was said, was originally MacNiel. The first of that name who settled in the village was out in the Rebellion of 1715, and he may have been a farrier in one of the Highland regiments that marched through the hills, or he may have been on the tramp for work when peace came. Finding this a snug nest he took up his abode, and founded a race of blacksmiths who resided for generations here. John Niel, the father of Henry, on a journey through the Greenlaw Moor, had a strange experience, which influenced his mind, and became to him and his family a reality.

As he was approaching the south side of Dirrington Law from Cattleshiel direction to come into the road to the village, he saw a strange animal, with a strange rider on its back. This may have been the result of his imagination working on the effects of moorland and sky, or it may have been some optical illusion, but when he approached Dronshiel, he met Robert Wilson of Blacksmill, and seriously asked him if he had met this unearthly equestrian. This adventure was related to his family, and so convinced were they all of the truth of this report that it became a trial for them to cross this moor, lest some evil would befall them. So when comrades of the blacksmith called to the girl gypsy to read his fortune, their minds were preoccupied with this story.

Was it the gypsy mother who foretold the fate of that winsome girl whose days were suddenly ended in the Nickering Pool? A young man was betrothed to a hill-maid, and one summer evening they went for a walk, which ended on the banks of the Dye, at the deep Nickering Pool.

They sat down to rest, and in the midst of loving conversation, the youth wished to steal from the girl a pledge of his affection. She started back to get out of his reach, and fell into the pool and was drowned. But let us return. Show your palm now, Henry Niel, to the gypsy girl, and let us know what is your fate.

Henry was a tall, strong, muscular man, and an intelligent and deft workman. About the fall of the year he went on a journey on foot to Floors Castle, to settle his account for work done with the factor of the Duke of Roxburghe. Returning homewards, he reached the town of Greenlaw, lying asleep on the outside slope of the Lammermuirs, where the Blackadder issues from the heathery uplands. It is a quaint old town, whose inhabitants have strong characteristics, which are frequently displayed in their public meetings, on local affairs, and in their political tendencies. They have the spirit of inquiry, and love of knowledge, and the true Scotchman's enthusiastic desire to rise in the world. Resting in the place, and inspecting the mail coach which rattled into the quiet street in the afternoon, Henry Niel wended his way up the hill, and entered the moor, passed on to his left the castle rings, where the townsfolks were wont to play their quoit matches on high days, and soon left all signs of human life behind him, as he penetrated this solitude for a seven mile walk. There is no made road through this bewildering moor, but as carts and other vehicles occasionally cross it for a near route, there are old ruts and marks of horses' hoofs to guide the wayfarer. In broad daylight and bright sunshine it is a lonely enough walk, but if a mist come suddenly down, even in the month of June, the traveller may occupy his time in wandering a whole night, and risk his life through excitement and fatigue. A man has been known to leave Greenlaw on a fine summer evening, and before he was aware of it, a dense mist overtook him, and he wandered up and down in the moss ground on the moorland, but always trying to keep on the west side of the 'Kames', those curious pier-like natural embankments, which run along the side of the boggy ground, lest he might enter the open moor and leave all landmarks for his guidance. Before he recovered his ground it was eight o'clock the next morning, and the sun had lifted the mist to enable him to make out his way towards Bedshiel, and thence to his home in the village. On the occasion of the election of a Member of

Parliament for the county, on the old system, a shepherd who was joint tenant of Bedshiel, crossed to Greenlaw to record his vote, when Sir Hugh Campbell[2] was returned, and on his way home a snowstorm came on, and in the deadly drift he perished. But it was neither mist nor snow that Henry Niel encountered on that fateful night, as he approached the Foul burn near Cattleshiel road. He was out of the worst part of the moor, when a more overpowering enemy seized him, and he had to surrender to it. It seemed to have been his excited imagination. Imagination is like fire - a good servant but a bad master. In this case it became his master and he yielded to it. The cloud that had settled on his family from the superstitious leanings of the father did its work effectually here. He never left the moor alive, and his mind during the night lost its balance. He had imagined that he was going to bed, for his clothes had been taken off, and he was found as if he had been dressing, and some of the garments were put on reversed.

As the gypsy party stand in front of the inn in their free and easy attitudes, Henry Niel and his friends sit and throw bantering words at them. Then they wend their way up the hill, intending to take up their quarters in a wood on the Haddington road, near the gate leading to the farm at Redpath. This wood is enclosed by a dyke, and with its old stumps and straggling decaying trees, it looks now in the distance not unlike an old unused churchyard. In the hill districts the clouds of superstition still hang, or did so at no distant date. About this time a boy found on the Rawburn Moor four one-pound notes, which were supposed to have fallen from the pocket of some sportsman when he was at the shooting. The lad gave the notes into the safekeeping of a shepherd on the farm, who put them in a safe drawer in his house. But some hand accustomed to pry into the secrets of his neighbour, fell upon them and took them away. The boy's father was recommended to go to Berwick and consult a 'spae-wife'[3] on the matter, and she very shrewdly and wisely told him to return and make this known in the district. This was done, and the prying hand one day deposited the notes inside the window of the house where he found them. Not more than twenty years ago, an intelligent old man lost a five-pound note as he was on the way to the village grocer to buy his usual supply of goods. He went to Berwick to recover his lost money through the medium of a 'spae-wife'.

She took him into a room, and told him to look into a mirror and he would see the man that had found the note. He did so, and a face that had certainly come behind him was seen. He returned home after having paid a fee for his advice, but the lost note never came to his hand.

But to resume. In the meantime some stragglers arrive from the farms, and a kind of committee has now been formed for the annual handball match[4] that is to be played between the folk of the Lammermuirs and the folks of the Lothians, on the moorland about halfway between the village and Gifford. The next morning was bright and warm, and the sky promised a fine day for the handball players, as they marched up the road at an early hour to meet their opponents, on the slope of a hill looking towards the Lothians. Their fellow-villagers were up early to see them off, and wish them success and victory. There was a good muster on both sides, and during the first part of the day they had the best of it, as the Lothian lads were again and again driven back with loss. By mid-day the heat of the sun was telling on their energies, and their bare feet became tired and sore. They rested for a time and partook of refreshments, which had been brought with them in a cart. The prospect before them was wide and varied, and looked like a beautiful panorama. From west to east, and onwards to the sea, the landscape was rich in natural greenery. The wide fields in the lowlands were covered with growing crops and fenced with trim hedgerows, and here and there sheltered and adorned with strips of plantation. The limits on the north and east were fringed by the sea which cast its waves in foam on the beach, and far away big ships looked like toys on the bosom of the deep. North Berwick Law, with its graceful outline, the Bass, immersed like a sea monster, and Tantallon, perched on a high rock by the sea, were objects on which the eye rested, while inland the Garelton Hills and Traprain varied the view. The Tyne flowed on to the sandy bay of Belhaven like a silver thread. In the afternoon their leader, James Hogg, lost heart and gave up the match, but John Craise took it in hand, and after a severe struggle they were defeated.

> "But Hogg our chief commander,
> The muirland lads did say,
> Acted his part like Johnny Cope,
> And homewards fled away.

But Craise like noble Grecian,
Did soon supply our loss,
While we in shirt and trousers
Ran barefoot o'er the moss."

When they came within sight of the village, the evening was delightful. The sun was like a ball of gold in the west, and over it hung variegated clouds like waves. The village lay in the hollow, set in greenery, and the blue smoke ascended in straight columns, showing the stillness of the balmy air, scented with the hay-making which was still going on around. The heather on the surrounding moor was giving signs of assuming its rich purple dress, which was the better displayed through the mass of green brackens growing there. The flocks of sheep dotted the whole scene. The sound of play and games arose from the village. It was indeed a scene of rural life and beauty, and the close of that summer day lingered lovingly in their view.

George Sherriff was standing outside his door when the party returned, but, as they had lost the day, their enthusiasm was at a low temperature, and they were glad to get to their houses for food and rest. The tailor was up the same evening at the school-house as George Sherriff was getting himself measured for a new pair of knee-breeches, and he was very particular about having an exact fit, for he had sufficient pride in being well and comely dressed. They remarked, in conversation about the minister, that a very marked change had come over him since the appearance of his son at the manse. He seemed more cheerful, and his step was quite elastic as he walked smartly up the hill from the village. But appearances such as these in a man of his years are often illusory, and so they turned out to be in this case.

It was a blink of sunshine before the close of day. One afternoon he had been busy in his garden, and he was telling Jenny Chapman of the amount of work he had accomplished, and how well and flourishing all the different crops were looking. The robin too, had been out in his company, and its briskness seemed to reciprocate his own feeling. That night, at prayers, he was particularly earnest and devout, and in saying 'good night' to Jenny he seemed to linger, as if he wished to make a communication to her, but she went off without his carrying it out. When morning came, and the forenoon sun was shining with dazzling brightness, they found him in his last sleep.

The news went round like a sudden thunderclap, and the parish seemed hushed for a while. Poor Jenny - who may have had some lingering tenderness for the minister beyond that of a servant to a master - was drowned with grief, and at odd moments, as she fulfilled her now dreary task, one could see her in covert corners, using her striped apron to check the tears which came unbidden to her eyes. George Sherriff felt that a spoke had been cruelly wrenched from his wheel of life, which was now approaching fast to the bottom of the hill, and it was many a day before he could get the sad fact mellowed for ordinary endurance.

Months went by, and the exuberance of summer was fast yielding to the decay of late autumn, which found Jenny Chapman in her own home in an old cottage in the village, which had its gable-end clothed with thick ivy that harboured the birds and sheltered them in frosty weather. A certain respectability hung around her, and her neighbours showed her an amount of deference which came to her from the position she had so long occupied in the manse. The robin went back to the ivied wall, and its mate was better pleased at this agreeable change. Such is the selfishness that lodges in the breast of bird nature as well as in human. Sometimes in its flight it would perch at the outside of the mill door, and the inoffensive miller would wink at the number of sparrows, robins, blackbirds and crows that would come to taste his stray corn. On other occasions the robin would fly with others to the ivy on the gable, and it was believed that he had discovered his old friend in her changed circumstances. When the leaves were embrowned, and the east wind shook them off the trees, it was very dreary to see the manse in its lonely and deserted state. The rose bushes beat themselves upon the shuttered windows, the wind moaned around the corners as it lifted the fallen leaves in its playfulness, and then on it went up the glen to howl under the door of the shepherd's cot, where the recumbent collies would start from their dozing and growl, as if one unknown was going to enter and disturb the family at their evening prayers, when the grey-haired and somewhat stern-looking father might be reading, *"The wind bloweth where it listeth, and thou hearest the sound thereof, but canst not tell whence it cometh and whither it goeth."*

Meeting of Watch and Dye (Sketch)

Notes - Glimpse IX

[1]. **Henry Niel.** He was born in 1781 to John Niel and Janet Lunham. The events which led to his death took place in 1817. It is sometimes stated that Henry was a rough, intemperate character. His grandfather, Robert had to apologise to the session and absolve to restrain from cursing and swearing and two of his uncles were reprimanded for fighting on the Sabbath - maybe they were too colourful for a small, rural village. The story of Henry Niel's death is a well-known one in Berwickshire. A full version of the story can be read in "The Haunted Borders" by Norrie McLeish (Alba Publishing 1997).

[2]. **Sir Hugh Hume Campbell.** Born 1812. Eldest son of Sir William Hume-Campbell by Charlotte, widow of F.Hall Esq. He was educated at Eton and Trinity College, Cambridge. He succeeded as the 7th baronet in 1833. (The 6th Baronet adopted the matrimonial name of Hume-Campbell on succeeding to the estate and dropped the name Purves.) He married Margaret daughter of John Spottiswoode Esq. of Spottiswoode who died in 1839. His second wife was Juliana Rebecca Fuller. He was M.P. for Berwickshire between1834 and 1847.

[3]. **Spae-wife.** a female fortune-teller.

[4]. **Handball match.** Handball or football matches had their origins in the Middle ages and perhaps even earlier. Often there were about a hundred players on either side. In the Borders where such matches were very popular they were often used as an excuse for a gathering of young men prior to a foray into England. They were gradually discontinued as the nineteenth century progressed, but the tradition still lives on in Jedburgh where they have an annual 'Ba' Game'.

Longformacus

Glimpse X

Two score years and more have passed. Children who were tightly packed in their cradles, the work of the village joiner, are now in the heyday of their strength and beauty; young men and maidens, whom we left courting on the summer eves by the ferny banks of the Dye, are now grandfathers and grandmothers, and with their experience of changeful years, they are trying to fill a stocking with bank-notes, for the support of their declining days. Those who have been set aside from the tumult of life have been gathered to their fathers, and they are better remembered by the roughly carved memorial stone, than by the frail neglectful memory of their surviving fellows. And through all the grades, during that eventful time, some have fallen unexpectedly by the way. The old sun-dial on the southern corner of the Auld Kirk, with blinks and blazes of sunshine, has noted the seasons, and has silently borne witness to the coming and going of men and manners on this remote parochial stage, and it has persistently held its face to the warm south, as if it looked for better times, although inherent in the human heart the notion lurks that those times are more in the past than in the future.

The beadle has pulled the rope down the gable-end, and rung the old bell for many a Sunday, to summon the folks from village and hill-farm, until it has been renewed again and yet again. But the sun dial did not look in vain, for from the sunny southern seas came one in whom were mingled a deal of Scotch shrewdness and the warm generous instincts of another race. And he came from the land which is proverbial for gold, or what can be converted into it. One Sunday, as the bell was tolling its last notes, a stranger on horseback appeared in the midst of the loungers on the bridge and at the church door, and with thoughtful consideration, William Wanless, the schoolmaster, who seeing that some information was wanted by the visitor went forward and supplied him.

The horseman marked him, and in future years became to him a faithful friend. The person was under the middle height, with a full mouth and dark eyes, and a somewhat swarthy complexion. His name was David Wardlaw Brown[1], and he soon became known as the Laird of Longformacus. He bought the property, with its old mansion surrounded by some fine ancestral trees, for the sum of £30,000, and this was considered a good price for the quality of the land and the valued rent. At the present time it would be interesting to know how much it would draw if it were put under the hammer of Walton and Lee. But as the laird was drawing a large income from his property in Penang, he could afford to pay a sum beyond its value, and also expend considerable sums on its improvement. This he at once set himself out to do. The 'Big House' was overhauled and modernised. The grounds were re-modelled, and a new avenue was run from the front of the house to the top of the village where the lodge stands. The road from the bridge to the Blacksmill burn was cut off at the Kirk, and a new road called the Caldra road was substituted for it. But the old road running through the fields by the river-side is still considered a right of way, and may be claimed by the people. The field on the left bank of the river, and sloping towards it, was converted into a beautiful garden. The schoolmaster had formerly rented this, and he and his pupils and villagers would delve, and plant, and sow it for his own use.

The tradesmen from the town of Dunse had reason to rejoice over the many jobs which were going on in the hill village. The promoters of health, through the reconstruction of the houses and drainage, had reasons to rejoice, but the lovers of the picturesque in the old thatched cottages had much reason to mourn. Down went the old cottages with their straw roofs, the open drains disappeared, and the banks of the Dye were planted with shrubs, and a wall was built in front of the 'row', making it a clean and tidy roadway. There was work for the people and to spare. The new bridge which had been thrown over the river by Adam Darling, in 1820, had its strength and solidity sufficiently tested by the amount of traffic that crossed it. The farm of Caldra changed its features by getting a new house and steading, and the farm of the Mill did the same.

William Moscrop and his wife Ailie[2] were busy with many

customers and William, bent like a bow, would in the evenings in his parlour erect himself like an arrow, and face his customers with some strong remark, on the usefulness of money, which in the hands of a reformer, becomes a decided blessing. But Willie's enthusiasm came to grief. As he was driving a cart for the work that was going on at the garden wall, he was wedged between the cart and the wall, and the accident caused his death. The pair were well known in the Lammermuirs, and on Sundays farm carts put up at their inn, and farmers and their families went into the parlour to get refreshments, in the form of biscuits and ale. When any customers during the week got rather the worse of liquor, Willie would whisper quietly to his wife, *"Ailie, gie them Dye noo."* In this way it might be said that *"Willie set his reputation on a cast, and stood the hazard of the Dye."*

The old thatched school and schoolhouse were levelled with the earth, except where part of the old clay wall was used, and good buildings were erected, which are a prominent feature on the outskirts of the village. the floor of the school was paved with blocks of wood like stones in a street, but this proved to be a failure, as the wood began to rot, and the blocks fell down below the original level. This made the floor uneven, and at the junction of the blocks an amount of dust collected which could not be thoroughly swept away.

But come into the field on this fine morning in early spring. The forecast of fine weather is in the air, and in field and wood. A number of men are busily employed in the work of draining, and the songs of the cheerful birds enliven them as they dig. They are suddenly startled by a voice in their vicinity. It is that of the Laird's, and he has come out to have a smoke and a chat with his men. He seats himself on the side of the drain, and gets what information he can out of the workers, besides the news of the hills. He flings to them cigars and lets them smoke away, as he feels that what is relished by himself will be relished by them. And so the hours go by, till it is time to leave off for dinner. A coachman in his employment got the worse of drink over and over again. He is repeatedly forgiven, and in this respect David Wardlaw Brown showed in himself a fine example of the highest Christian graces. The mistress of his house threatened to dismiss a cook, as the lady of the house will sometimes do when the servant is incompetent or neglectful of her duties. He protested against this conduct, and expressed himself as ashamed of the treatment. But that same mistress, whose home is now in an ancient historic mansion, has many amiable qualities, and has gathered her old servants round her, where they cling to her in her later years, as they did in her former years, and some have gone down into the dark valley, soothed by the kindness of her home and friendship.

Here is another trait of the laird's character. One misty night, as the carriage was coming from a dinner party, the laird was afraid that the coachman would capsize the carriage over the hill at the Snuffy Hole. He got out and mounted the box, and took the management of the reins. He did not drive far when he set the whole party over the height. They walked home over the wet and dirty roads in dinner dress, and were carefully attended to by James Lauder[3], the butler, who was long in their employment, and was much valued as a trustworthy official. In his years, in the Black Bull Hotel, Dunse, he was much respected, and his intelligent and venerable appearance was very noticeable there. James Darling was the land steward, and before he went off to Australia, he drove up one day to the door of the schoolhouse in the laird's carriage, stepped out, and informed William Wanless that the laird had desired him to accompany the steward to London to visit the Metropolis, and see the great exhibition, and to help him to do this, he presented him with twenty sovereigns. One may say that this was well spent money for the parish, as the mind of the schoolmaster would benefit by the excursion, and thereby the scholars in the end.

And now the Rev. Walter Weir, with his nimble and alert figure, was seen going the round of his parochial duties. He was the pattern of neatness and punctuality, and as he had been trained in his early years to business habits, he was orderly and methodical. His pulpit appearance was characterised by solemnity and gentle persuasion, and his discourses were thoroughly evangelical and consoling. We may see him now, on a visit to the Lodge at the head of the village, to give the folks a word of sympathy in season.

There lived there at this time a man named Jeffrey[4], who cleaned the walks round the 'Big House', and did odd jobs. After the death of his first wife, he again married, although he had a grown-up family. The step-mother, who was a tall woman, did not lead a happy life, and one day her step-daughter and she quarrelled. It was supposed that the daughter kicked the mother on a part of the leg which was weak, for a blood-vessel burst and the woman bled to death in about five minutes. In connection with this incident, a strange thing occurred to John Brown[5], precentor and farmer at Townhead. One summer night a messenger came to his house, and desired him to go to Dunse to request Dr Campbell to hurry up to Byrecleugh on a professional visit. John Brown went out at once to catch a horse which was grazing in a field adjoining 'The Strips'. The horses had, however, strayed into the wood, and were feeding there. In his search he came within twenty yards or so of a queer object, somewhat like a 'cuddy'. He then halted. The object raised itself, and it turned out to be a tall woman dressed in black. A strange thrill ran through John's frame, and he became so terrified that he could not move. He called out to her, supposing her to be the tall woman who lived in the lodge, but who had been buried for six weeks. The woman did not answer, but came so close to him that he felt the smell of 'spirits'. Then like a flash of lightning, the thought came to him that this was a person who was on the way to the village as her father was dead. He turned in a moment to seek his horses. It seemed that this wanderer had gone into the wood to rest, as she was the worse of drink, and when the young farmer saw her on all fours, she was groping for a bundle she had dropped.

The ecclesiastical fever which ran through Scotland at the time of the Disruption[6] gradually reached this quiet spot in Lammermuir. A Free Church was built and a congregation was formed, and under the zealous catechist James Rathie[7], the little flock was kept together with as much tact and pawkiness as he had been wont to tend his sheep on the Cheviot Hills, when he wore the crook and plaid. In the summer and autumn months come, from the busy outside world, visitors with the aroma of business and city streets hanging about them, for change of air, rest and recreation by the banks of the Dye, where they may fish, muse or roam at large, as fancy may devise. And at times some rollicking and genial disciples of the brush and palette have set up their easels to the wondering gaze of the countryman, who in his own estimation sometimes put a value on the artist's work similar to that for painting a pair of cart wheels, or the embellishment of his water-barrel. It is an honour to the village to know that John R. Reid,[8]who has made his mark in the artistic world and founded a school of art for himself, was once a resident here for months, and by his frank and unassuming nature gained the esteem of many of those who made his acquaintance. And James Michael Brown[9], and John McIntyre - the one a rising Edinburgh artist, and the other an exhibitor in the Royal Academy, London - beguiled the leisure hours of some with friendly and witty conversation.

This secluded spot is so near and yet so far from the stir of life, that it may be said to be high and dry away from the tumult of the world and the tidal wave of busy men which surrounds it on all sides. The 'Flying Scotchman' thunders and screams along the eastern slopes of the Lammermuirs every day, within nine miles of it; the Berwickshire trains, comparing their speed with that of the London express, take things extremely easy as they amuse themselves within six miles of it; and the Midland express, within a distance of fifteen miles, bears with it an interchange of nationality as it rushes through the vale of Gala. Even the proposed new line, bringing trade and life within sound of the muirfowl at Gifford and Garvald, twelve miles away, is yet disinclined to enter the vale of Whitadder, to bring the heather heights cultivation, and to the inhabitants ease and prosperity. The life of the roaming shepherd, or the outdoor work of the trudging ploughman, enables him to hear sounds which are not an everyday occurrence. He tells that in certain states of the wind and atmosphere the rumbling train may be heard both on the east and southern sides, and at Cattleshiel the rolling of the surf on the seashore comes now and then to carry the thoughts away to the heaving expanse of ocean. At the Henley Hill, the time-gun on Edinburgh Castle has made itself heard, at a distance of thirty-four miles. A traveller leaving London by the night express may reach Berwick and proceed to Duns, and by the next forenoon be in the midst of as romantic, remote, and wild a glen as he could find in Argyle or Ross, and may find here a kind of earthly paradise during the summer and autumn months, when, in comparison with the bleakness of winter, it has made for itself a resurrection of sylvan life and rural beauty.

But in winter there is a marked contrast to this picture, and the severe snowstorms which frequently visit the uplands have a wonderful effect on various occupations and modes of life. Take the following example of an old-fashioned winter. A snowstorm began in the forenoon of a day in March, and the drifting was great. The wind blew from the east. Some carts from the farms went to Duns, and men from the village set out with shovels to help them home through the snow. The snowstorm still continued on the following day, and the powdery snow drifted fearfully. When the schoolmaster went into the school in the morning, four scholars were sitting at the fire. They had fought their way through the drift. They were sent home at once. All that night the storm continued. In the morning the sky was clear and frosty, and the doors of the school and schoolhouse were completely blocked with high wreaths of snow. No scholar appeared. In the forenoon the snow was removed from the doors, and the snow-plough cleared the roads through the village, and everything was ready for schoolwork the next morning, which brought no scholars from the distant farms. Men now began to cut a footpath through the snow at the lodge, and going towards Duns which enabled a man on horseback to go there. The men got as far as the entrance to 'The Strips' at the end of the day. A villager, who had gone to Duns on Monday, ventured to walk home on Wednesday, but had a great struggle on the journey. He brought some letters and two newspapers, a Daily Scotsman and a Standard. The postman had not appeared for three days. The snow where it was cut measured five feet deep. The next day the roads were still blocked, and the men were slowly going on with the work of cutting a path through the snow. The postman came after four day's absence with letters and newspapers. There was a lull in the storm for three days then snow began to fall, and there was a good deal of drifting. Some carts went as far as the Hardens and turned back. Two carts went from Rawburn on to Duns, but extra horses went off to meet them and help them home. The new snow on top of the old snow greatly increased the depth, and again effectually blocked the roads. Men again set out on the following day to cut a track through the snow, and at the end of the day's work they reached the Dronshiel Bridge. In some places the snow was piled up to the height of nine feet. But in a day or two a thorough thaw set in, and the Dye came roaring down in a high state of flood.

But though this type of weather was a sad drawback to many in Lammermuir, yet a set of men enjoyed weeks of it, when the roaring game at the curling pond went on with all the life and spirit which could possibly be exhibited by the keen curler. The sport began in the morning as regular as the clock, and ended as the sun set. Refreshments were provided by the laird, who was one of the keenest curlers of the club, which was founded by him forty years ago, and admitted into the Royal Caledonian Curling Club two years after. This is how the curling club appeared twenty years ago. The pond is situated in a retreat, sheltered on all sides by woods. Its surroundings are quaint. The north side is circled by feathery-looking firs with their tops cut short, but one here and there is allowed to rise to its natural height, which gives the whole a fanciful appearance. A round wooden house with thatched roof and overhanging eaves stands at one end, and through the open door there comes a warm glow from a stick fire, which blazes in a brazier in the centre of the floor. A faint blue smoke rises from the can above, and curls away in the still air. At the side of the house may sometimes be seen a venerable donkey eating hay, and now and again looking around him with stolid indifference, while his young masters in knickerbockers, and full of holiday spirits, sport on the ice with a swarm of youngsters from the village.

The brawling of the river Dye is heard in the distance, and the robin hops about on a neighbouring branch, and thinks no doubt that it has seen better days. When the day draws to a close, the setting sun gleams through the trees, and by their interposition resembles the fiery mouth of a furnace. And today come trudging through the snow a compliment of the club from Whitchester on the hill, where another laird has transformed by taste and wealth, and by use of the trowel, the plane and the shrub, a waste place, and adorned it by trees shrubs and flowers, until, compared with what it was a quarter of a century ago, it now blossoms like the rose. A glimpse of the old place comes back. A low-roofed farmhouse is surrounded by a few stunted trees. The cot houses are a sad wreck. Rain comes in and trickles down the walls, and daylight looks in through chinks in the gable, where the family sits at the fire. Poverty and pride are an ill-matched pair, and like the scales of the village grocer, families rise and fall, and at one time this one is up, and the other is down, and so runs the world away.

Glimpse X Notes

[1]. **David Wardlaw Brown**. (1812-1864). His parents were David Brown, landed proprietor, and Lucy Grace. His wife was Margaret Turnbull Tait (1816-1891) whom he married in 1837. David Wardlaw Brown made his fortune in Penang, in what is now Malaysia. He bought the estate of Longformacus in 1847 and spent a considerable amount of his time and money on it. He was for a while the Deputy Lieutenant of Berwickshire. Held in high regard by his peers it was said of him: "... and if ever a man lived on earth of whom it may be justly said he died without an enemy, it was David Browne of Longformacus."

[2]. **William Moscrop.** (1783-1849). His wife was Alison Currie who died a month before him at the age of 76. In 1815 they were forced to appeal for poor relief and were given 1/- by the Kirk Session.

[3]. **James Lauder.** Born 1815 in the parish of Fogo. His wife's name was Christina and he had a son James, who was born in 1859

[4]. **William Jeffrey.** Born in Fogo in 1798. In the 1861 Census he is described as "a lodge keeper, formerly gardener". He was a widower living with his daughter, Mary, who was then aged 28 and who acted as his housekeeper.

[5]. **John Brown**. Born in Jedburgh in 1816. In the 1861 Census he is described as a "farmer of 100 acres". With him were his wife, Elizabeth, aged 51 and their son, John, aged 24.

[6]. **The Great Disruption**. In 1843 forty percent of the Church of Scotland ministers marched out of the General Assembly and set up a new church - the Free Church of Scotland. Disputes within the Established Church had been flaring up for many years between the Evangelical wing, who regarded themselves as the spiritual heirs of the Covenanters, and the Moderates, who were more flexible in doctrine and more amenable to government directives. In 1834 the General Assembly

had passed the Veto Act which gave the congregation the right to reject the local patron's nominee for a ministerial vacancy. The government declared this to be unlawful, but despite this many congregations rejected the nominees of their patrons. The new church had to finance its ministers and build its own schools entirely from voluntary contributions. For a while it looked as if the Church of Scotland would lose its pre-eminent position. But financial problems and disagreements were eventually to see the re-uniting of the Free Church and the Church of Scotland in 1929. A minority, "The Wee Frees", remained, but they were mainly restricted to the Highlands and Islands. The Border parishes were less affected than other places by the Disruption.

7. **James Rathie.** (1803-1869). His first wife was Isabella Johnston (1818-1862). His second wife was Elizabeth Mack who died at Rawburn in at the age of 60 in the same year as her husband. He had a son born in 1854 named James Johnstone Rathie. Another son, William, died in Duns in 1869 at the age of 16. James Rathie was a Free Church catechist for 24 years and had been in Longformacus for 20 years. At the start he preached to his congregation in a barn but eventually a church was built and a congregation formed. He died at Rawburn, well known and respected throughout the district.

8. **John R. Reid.** (1851-1926). Born in Edinburgh. Moved to Cornwall in 1881 and then to London in 1901. His subjects were mainly field-workers and humble people.

9. **James Michael Brown.** (1854-1957. Born in Edinburgh. Painted landscapes mostly water-colours. Well-known for his golfing scenes in East Lothian.

William Wanless

One summer day in the month of May, 1866, there stood in the little churchyard of Longformacus a large company of mourners, who had laid in the grave the remains of William Wanless, parish schoolmaster. The trees which enshroud the graveyard rustled gently overhead; the rooks from their drowsy cawing seemed to feel the influence of the balmy air; and the waters of the Dye, clear and sparkling, murmured and prattled in their course; the merry birds and the very insects, bee and butterfly, were joyous and free. But the grave was soon closed, and the company quietly dispersed. That night in manse, farmer's parlour, shepherd's cottages scattered over the moor, and in village homes, words of affection and gratitude were expressed towards the worthy old man who had served a people well and faithfully for forty-five years, and words of sympathy for the family who were no more to inhabit the dear schoolhouse that had been to them always a pleasant home. A tree that has grown for half a century must have established itself firmly in the soil. It may be cut down, the chief root may be torn up, but there will remain shoots implanted in the ground which will defy the labourer to dig out. And so a good man who has dwelt in one place for forty-five years must, from our natures, have entwined himself round the hearts of those who were to him, children, men and women. He may be taken away, but there will be found in the living, fresh memories of the dead. No wonder that William Wanless is yet enshrined in the corner of many a heart in the Lammermuirs, and also far away.

Sometime in the autumn of 1821, a young man of twenty-three years of age, under the middle height and dark complexioned, arrived in the village of Longformacus, and not long after this he brought with him a young and ruddy-faced wife, when they took up their residence in the schoolhouse. These were William Wanless and Margaret Graham. They had travelled from Cousland in Midlothian, where William had been teacher, and where he had fallen in love. The schoolhouse was then a small thatched cottage, consisting of two rooms and a garret. The school was likewise limited in its dimensions, poorly furnished and uncomfortable, but somewhat like the country schools of those days. Here then the young couple began housekeeping, and we can fancy the young wife putting her house to 'rights', and pondering over the management of her new home, and the young schoolmaster busied with his scholars at the opening of the session of 1821, and anxious to feel his way among them and the people of the parish.

Children trudged for miles to the village from distant farms and shepherds' cottages, and as weeks passed away the school was comfortably filled. Longformacus was then a mean, untidy village of low, thatched houses, ornamented in front and rear with peat stacks, and pigsties, and middens. In wet weather and dark nights, it required some skill to walk abroad without stepping to the ankles in mud and pools of water. As the young schoolmaster was making progress in the schoolwork, and feeling full of life and spirits, the winter drew on. In school he was hearty, industrious, and anxious about the education of his flock. Then the long nights were spent in homely talk, parochial duties, and occasional visits to the villagers, and in forming plans for the future.

Disappointment came apace, heavy snowstorms burst upon the inhabitants of the hills, and made the roads to Duns and elsewhere impassable, kept scholars warm by their own hearths, and reduced the numbers at school. New Year came, and Old Handsel Monday quickly followed, and yet the snow was deep and the frost keen and established. The dreary time was enlivened by an annual gathering in the village inn. The company consisted of fathers, mothers, grown-up sons and daughters, and children. They danced, sang, and spent the night as innocently as any large family party. William Wanless was not absent; his jovial, social disposition, made him welcome, and his presence was also a mark of approbation. Strait-laced moralists or hypocrites may sneer at these assemblies, but liberality of thought will grant them to an honest, industrious, and sober people.

The snows of winter melted as spring appeared, and the muddy waters of the Dye rushed out and roared through the village, and curious spectators might be seen bending over the bridge and gazing with wonder at the swollen tide. Then the fields and roads soon dried under the influence of wind and sunshine. The school work went on again with vigour. The system of examination by clergymen of the Presbytery was in its glory, and the schoolmaster exhibited the results of his labours, broken and disturbed by irregular attendance through the rigours of winter. The fine weather had hardly set in when field and pastoral work thinned the ranks at school, and the teacher devoted the summer and early autumn months to the instruction of those who were left, because they were unable to earn a shilling to increase the family purse.

And so passed the time away. The events of one year so resembled those of another in the life of William Wanless, that we have little to record beyond certain landmarks in the family history. Before the year 1848 had begun, the schoolhouse was lively with the prattle of childhood, and noisy with the buoyant spirits of boys and girls. Out of a family of seventeen, four died young, and thirteen survived their parents. The struggle to rear so many was tough. Who shall reveal the heartache and economy, which were brought to bear on the plans to keep them in bread and respectability? In those times the salary of the teacher was a trifle, and a living was eked out of it - school fees and emoluments which were derived from other parochial duties. Is the office of a teacher of so little consequence that he should have, in the midst of his daily toil, secret fears and doubts of sufficient income for the wants of his household? Education in our time has been well weighed in the balance, and schoolmasters are watching the process which ought to raise their positions worthy of the work to which they devotedly give their lives.

Rev. Walter Weir

In the calm seclusion of our hill life, years run away without leaving many landmarks for the memory to dwell on, beyond those of individual interest. The seasons come and bring with them the everlasting touch of nature. The seasons go and return with the same glad welcome. We have, as a community, a good share of enjoyments, few cares, and not many desires which cannot be attained. And we may sometimes think in our foolishness that this smooth pastoral existence will continue for ever, and represent a golden age which the human heart loves to picture. But there comes at wide intervals a visitor who dispels this fancy and makes our thoughts turn inwards. Death is the visitor, and it has come here when everything is springing into life and beauty, and taken from us a good and holy man.

The time is memorable. The Rev. Walter Weir died at the manse on Monday the 10th April 1871, at half past five o'clock in the afternoon. On Thursday evening, the 30th ult., Mr Weir was engaged on the good old style of making his annual visitation on every family in the parish. He had visited a number of houses in the village on that evening, and was evidently in better health than usual. On Friday morning he complained of a sudden pain in his temples, and became so ill that he could hardly go upstairs to his bedroom. Dr McWatt, Dunse was called in, and we soon knew that a shock of paralysis had struck our minister down at the age of seventy-five. From the first the hopes of his recovery were doubtful. But we are prone to hope, and though we thought that Mr Weir would no longer speak to us with earnest voice from the pulpit, we desired, and with our hearts, that he would recover and be able to give us a glimpse of the sunshine of his gentle nature.

A week wore away, and there seemed to be a turn in the tide of the disease. He became more conscious and had a better appetite. But the appearances were deceitful. A state of fever set in and affected his general health. This continued until he gradually sank. His spirit departed so gently that those in the sick chamber thought he had gone to sleep. A mirror was placed to his lips. It remained unstained. He had gone to sleep for ever.

During the ten days of Mr Weir's illness there was a shadow of gloom on all in the neighbourhood, and that shadow was deepened by the sad news of his decease. We have sustained a true loss in the death of the Rev. Walter Weir, and we deplore much the want of the earnest minister, the kind friend, the tender man. He was eminently a man of piety. The office of a minister is open to the eyes of the world, and the evil tongue of man cannot be held from speaking of any flaws in the mail; but the keenest eye could find no weak link in the armour of godliness which has been girt on Mr Weir through a long life spent in the service of Him who is the essence of all purity.

There come to us records of his early life, his college days, his probationary years, his public ministry, his private life, and all these records tell us that a good and pious man has left us. His religion did not set him on a platform and make him an object of dread. He went in and out among the people, and was regarded as a familiar friend, ready at all times to give assistance by cheering words and kindly deeds. And in this free intercourse the same respect was given to the homely friend as to the pious minister.

Mr Weir was a man under the middle height, and of a light and active figure. His last visit was made to the village with the same nimbleness and activity which characterised his youth. We see him now, and the same figure will start up at our wish at any time, and to such a pitch of reality as to haunt the bodily sense. He comes to us in full dress of spotless black. His white necktie is rolled after a fashion of an earlier date. His head is somewhat thrown back and face uplifted, and his locks are as white as snow. His light blue eyes look through a pair of glasses set in gold. He carries a cane with an ivory head, and a white

Pomeranian dog runs beside him.

Mr Weir was the author of two volumes called "The Highway of Holiness," and "The Fruits of Europe unto Christ." These bear the same stamp of holiness and integrity of heart which pervaded his whole life. They are the fruits of his experience in the Christian world. The Rev. Walter Weir was the son of Robert Weir, merchant, Leith. After his course at college was ended, he filled for some time the pulpits at Innerwick, and Cupar, Fife. In 1837 he was ordained minister of the parish of Walls and Flotta in Orkney. He remained there eleven years. There he married Jane McCormick Hill, daughter of the late Professor Hill, St. Andrews, and when they settled in Longformacus their son and only child was one year old. His son is now the Rev. Robert W. Weir, minister of Greyfriars, Dumfries. Mr Weir used to recall his sojourn in the far north with feelings of pleasure. How kindly he talked of the intelligent Orcadians, their seafaring, perilous life; the fine rock scenery, and the great sea which sounded on the beach in front of the manse.

And in the corner of his Master's vineyard, he has given for seven-and-twenty years his whole heart, soul, strength, and mind to his duty to God and man, according to his high standard of a minister of the Gospel. His life was a living sermon preached to everyone with affectionate and tender love. The good which he has done is written on the hearts of many, and will bear fruit for years to come. And now at the close of life's short day they have laid him in a green spot between two old gnarled trees in the old churchyard; and as these elms bend their aged arms over his last home, they seem to do it in benediction to the good man who has gone to rest under their shade. And in the warmth of our hearts may we cull a flower from that precious gift to us, "The Sermon on the Mount," and place it on a memorial stone, and let it be these fitting words, "Blessed are the pure in heart, for they shall see God."

Postscript

It is a beautiful autumn day, and we have left the great and picturesque city to visit a neighbouring village with its fete, fountains and palace. We sit on the terrace and watch the amusements and the many phases of human life. Historic associations crowd around us from the gay capital and the village, until the very air seems filled with pictures of the past. A homely-looking priest passes along, engrossed in friendly chat with a fair damsel. My comrade scans the pair with critical eyes, and my thoughts are distracted by the words, "Look! look!" and the pointing of a finger. There before my eyes is the priest's foot encased in an ill-fitting shoe, and as the foot rises and falls, I notice a big hole in the heel of his black stocking, and the flesh of the foot is seen like the colour of a cut salmon.

These 'Glimpses' are built on the rock of truth, and illumined by the light of imagination, and they may conjure up to some happy years, and beloved scenes, and the spirits of the past come once again to cheer them in this wayward world.

My First Visit

The Quad is almost silent now,
There is no chance of college row.
They come like pigeons and like rooks,
To feed on lectures and on books,
Then over many lands are blown,
Godlike to soar, or be unknown.
I longed to be away from town,
Weary with hacking up and down.
So leaving pavement hard as rocks,
I hurried out to Lothian folks.
Nature was in its luscious prime,
All green and gold in Scottish clime,
My friend had suffered much in life,
Was settled now with bairns and wife,
Gentle of manner, strong of mind,
Had sympathy with human kind,
Had heard of an old parish "cure"
Across the way - o'er Lammermuir.
As bird in hand's worth two in bush,
Armed with youth, onward I push;
That night conversed we long and late
How best to hurry on my fate.

'T'was early on a brilliant morn,
'Mid sultry heat and waving corn,
I journeyed on through field, o'er rill,

And up the steep way towards the hill.
With sweeping view at my command,
O'er Lammermuirs own pasture land,
Behind the grey North Sea afar,
Beat on the great rocks at Dunbar.

Broad miles of moorland round me lay
As if old Nature was at play,
The sky fell down on ev'ry side
Over brown heath in stretches wide,
Where flocks of sheep browsed up and down
Unconscious of gay London town.
With miles and noontide heat oppressed,
On ancient stone I sat to rest,
And read the last sensation book.
Curious device its author took
When Greenwood donned the printer's dress,
To coin the "Casual" for the press.
The cry of whaup, the wild bee's hum,
The whirr of grouse like kettledrum,
The song of soaring lark in air,
Were to me sole companions there;
But gentle Hogg of Yarrow's stream
Was by my side as in a dream.

The ridge gave way. Down hill I went.
At Frierdykes glad half hour was spent
In shepherd's cot. At Bentydod,
A memorable land of Nod,
They late and early cut the corn,
'Tis said upon a New Year's morn.
Pursuing glen where Bothwell flows
Past Yardley, ev'ry shepherd knows,
And Crichness high with many flocks,

St Agnes - Suttie's shooting box,
I came to Cranshaws kirk and school,
With charming stream and fishing pool;
Its farm 'mid trees, castle on steep,
Are known all round as mountain keep,
Called by Sir Walter, kind and good,
Fair Lucy Ashton's Ravenswood.

Brisk Whitadder flowed fast along,
And cheered lone Cranshaws with its song,
My brother's welcome came in need,
'T'was hospitality indeed.
But Cranshaws long has had this fame
Since Royal James of roving name.
The stranger's glamour, or his mien,
Unusual in the scanty scene,
Puzzled the priest, and on that day
For Stuart James he did not pray,
So coat of arms engraved on stone
Immortalised his shaky throne.

My head I held to Dirrington,
And dropped on road from Haddington,
Where Robbie Burns - poetic swell,
On Border tour to Berrywell,
Might pause and scan the rural scene,
With hill, and moor, and hollow dene,
Where village lay in sylvan rest
Beside the Dye, whose rippling breast,
From pebbly bed and monster stone,
Gives murmurs loud in monotone.
'Bout rock at bridge this legend goes,
A giant and the deil grew foes
At cards; and in the midst of play,

My First Visit

The deil was in a losing way,
Down went the cards and up the gains,
And to give the prig his pains,
At him was flung the monster stone,
Which well-nigh tossed him from his throne.

A kirk on left, a kirk on right,
Often is anomalous sight
In rural spots, which cry aloud
For Guthrie keen, and true M'Leod,
To hoist the Union Flag for aye,
And quell the wranglings of the day.
My legislator, parson, friend,
There's something here must need amend;
People may rant about their creeds,
The soul of life is in its deeds.

Nearer the Church, farther from grace,
Reverse it and you have this case.
A stout dame bade me climb the hill,
And pass the Inn and Andrew's Mill,
Where aunt of Jeanie Deans at ease,
Perchance had curdled ewe milk cheese.
Two furlongs up a winding way,
In rustic style the old manse lay,
With variegated view to eye,
Of hill and moor, of Watch and Dye.
On garden seat, 'neath shady tree,
A lady, knitting, fronted me,
With all the grace of courteous France
Conducted me into her manse,
Where pastor neat, and dressed with care,
With gentle good, and pious air,
And heart on sleeve, me captive took,

And holds in life a sacred nook.

Near Craigie's sloping wooded side
Is poet's corner, there the pride
Of Home of "Douglas," once renowned,
Who mused on "Norval" to the sound
Of Dye's own music and the breeze,
Through shaggy fir and old beech trees.

As charity begins at home,
We'll hang some pictures round our dome.
Removed from village stands the school
Where homely Wanless held his rule
So long and well in days of yore,
And for the young winnowed good store
Of grain, hoed weeds so rife,
And trained the stems for after life.
In Helen's Isle when old Nap died,
Young Wanless to the village hied
With blooming wife and spirits high,
To mind the mote in his own eye
And not his neighbour's. And the tie
Of family in him was great.
He kept them all in decent state,
And working years full forty-five,
He slept. Hear it, my friends alive.

America was brewing war
Of separation, and the star
Of Union glimmered in the west,
When Sherriff at his manly best
Took reins in hand, and held them long
(To those worthies work seemed like song).
In school, in those days small and mean,

And often filled at Fast'en's e'en,
When horrid taste of eager folks
Was pleased with savage fighting cocks.
The beaten bird upon the floor
Was taken to the master's door,
Then tricky youngsters, men and all,
Engaged in field at rough football.
To eke out income rather scant,
And keep Jean Porteous from want,
An acre glebe annexed to school
Was delved by Sherriff as a rule.
Near fifty years at pen and book
Like aged chief he hung his crook.

But now the vista's dark and dim,
All living tongue is dead for him -
Rab Sharp, who in his childish glee,
At daring deeds of gone Dundee
Mayhap had played the soldier bold,
When Killiekrankie's tale was told;
At Holyrood when Charlie danced,
In manhood may have been entranced'
By story from some strolling loon,
About the turn-tail whig dragoon;
And ere the end of life's strange page;
He vaulted o'er the Bible age.
The trio in God's acre lie,
Vignettes for Gray's rare elegy,
Away from worry and from care,
Away from hurry, resting there.
In spring the rooks caw on the trees,
In summer blows the fragrant breeze,
In autumn waves the yellow corn,
In winter sounds the huntsman's horn;

All soon they go and come again,
Until old earth be onthe wane.

My little dog on sofa lies,
And watches me with kindly eyes.
So strange it is. When we begin
The journey here, we've nought laid in
Like bird and beast, which have a plan.
No map is folded out to man,
He gathers knowledge as he goes;
'Tis here from friends, and there from foes,
And when he's buckled for the fray
It's "au revoir" for other day.
But, brothers, to ourselves be true,
God is o'erhead for me, for you.

'Tis done. To workers in pure gold
This simple sketch may savour bold;
The mavis sweet sings on the tree,
To please itself, not you or me.

Index